Fiona Mapp

Success

AQA
GCSE Mathematics
Higher
Revision Guide

Contents

Contents

3

Collecting data

Data collection U1

The census is one of the largest data collection processes that takes place. The census is done every 10 years and its main aim is to give a 'snapshot' of Britain at the time. In order to carry out the census all households are given a survey to complete.

Types of data U1

There are two main types of data:

- **Quantitative**
  The answer is a number, e.g. How many blue cars are there in a car park?
- **Qualitative**
  The answer is a word, e.g. What is your favourite colour?

Quantitative data can be discrete or continuous:

- **Discrete data** has an exact value. Each category is separate and is usually found by counting. An example is the number of people with brown hair.

- **Continuous data** has values that merge from one category to the next. Examples include the heights and weights of students. Continuous data cannot be measured exactly. The accuracy of the measurement relies on the accuracy of the measuring equipment.

Primary data is data that is collected by the person who is going to analyse and use it. **Secondary data** is data that is available from an external source, such as books, newspapers and the internet.

Hypotheses and experiments U1

A hypothesis is a prediction that can be tested. Experiments can be used to test hypotheses.

For example:
Hypothesis: The better the light, the faster seedlings grow.
Variable: This is the intensity of the light, the condition that can be changed.

Conditions: The other conditions must stay the same. All seedlings must be exactly the same size, strength and colour to start with. If there is **bias** (e.g. if one side of the tray gets extra water), then the experiment is invalid and needs to start again.

Two-way tables U1

Data can be collected and displayed in a **two-way table**. This is a table in which data can be read horizontally and vertically. For example, the table shows the results of a survey of favourite sports of some students.

Even if the table is not fully complete, you may be able to work out any missing figures from the data that is available in the table.

	Football	Swimming	Hockey	Total
Female	12	11	6	29
Male	15	9	10	34
Total	27	20	16	63

Questionnaires U1

Questionnaires can be used to test hypotheses.

When designing questionnaires:

- Decide what you need to find out: the **hypothesis**.
- Give instructions on how the questionnaire has to be filled in.
- Do not ask for information that is not needed (e.g. name).
- Make the questions clear and concise.
- Keep the questionnaire short.
- If people's opinions are needed, make sure the question is **unbiased**.
  An example of a **biased** question would be: 'Do you agree that a leisure centre should have a tennis court rather than a squash court?'

- Include a time period if it is needed, for example, 'How many hours do you play computer games **per week**?'
- Allow for all possible answers. For example, if you were asking 'What is your favourite colour?', add an option for 'Other'.

When asked to design a questionnaire, always word the questions carefully. Try to avoid bias appearing in your questions.

Sampling U1

Sampling is an efficient way of collecting information about a large population. It is important that the sample is representative of the population and does not contain bias. The bigger the sample the more accurate the results will be.

There are two main methods of sampling.

- **Random sampling**
  In a random sample each member of the population has an equal chance of being chosen.
- **Stratified sampling**
  Usually the population is divided into groups (**strata**) that have something in common, such as age. A simple random sample is then taken from each group. The same proportion of the group is used for each sample.

Example

	Left-handed	Right-handed
Boys	14	34
Girls	12	40

The table shows the number of girls and boys in year 11 of a school. A stratified sample of size 30 is to be taken. Calculate the number of right-handed girls to be sampled.

14 + 12 + 34 + 40 = 100 students in total.

Fraction of population who are right-handed girls = 40

Number of right-handed girls in sample
$= \frac{40}{100} \times 30 = 12$

Quick test

1 Design a questionnaire you could give a friend in order to find out what they do in their spare time.

2 Colin is carrying out a survey on homework; he decides to use a stratified sample and ask 100 students. Calculate the number of students he will ask from each group.

	Frequency
Year 7	120
Year 8	150
Year 9	230

Representing data

Statistics and probability

Drawing pie charts | U1

Pie charts are used to illustrate data. They are circles split up into sections, each sector representing a certain category of the data or number of items.

Example
The table shows the favourite sports of 24 students in year 11. Draw a pie chart to show this data.

Sport	Frequency
Football	9
Swimming	5
Netball	3
Hockey	7
Total	**24**

Sport	Frequency	Angle	Workings
Football	9	135°	$\frac{9}{24} \times 360°$
Swimming	5	75°	$\frac{5}{24} \times 360°$
Netball	3	45°	$\frac{3}{24} \times 360°$
Hockey	7	105°	$\frac{7}{24} \times 360°$
Total	**24**	**360°**	

To calculate the angles for the pie chart:
- Find the total of the frequencies.
- Find the fraction of the total for each category.
- Multiply the fraction by 360° to find the angle.

Interpreting pie charts | U1

Example
The pie chart shows how 18 students travel to school.

How many students travel by:
a) car? 360° = 18 students
$$1° = \frac{18}{360°} = 0.05$$ Work out what 1° represents.
60° × 0.05 = 3 students
b) bus? 80° × 0.05 = 4 students
c) foot? 220° × 0.05 = 11 students

💡 *Pie chart questions are usually worth about 4 marks at GCSE. Make sure the angles add up to 360° before drawing a pie chart. Measure the angles carefully since you are allowed only a 2° tolerance.*

Line graphs | U1

A line graph is a set of points joined by lines.

Year	2004	2005	2006	2007	2008	2009
Number of cars sold	2500	2900	2100	1900	1600	800

Middle values, like point A, have no meaning. Point A does **not** show that halfway between 2006 and 2007, there were 2000 cars sold.

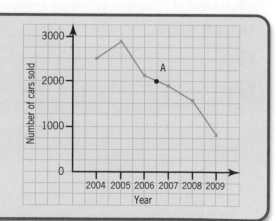

Histograms U1

Histograms illustrate **continuous data**. They are similar to bar charts except that there are no gaps between the bars. The data must be grouped into **equal** class intervals if the length of the bar is used to represent the frequency. Histograms are also known as frequency diagrams.

Mass (W kg)	Frequency
$45 \leqslant W < 55$	7
$55 \leqslant W < 65$	13
$65 \leqslant W < 75$	6
$75 \leqslant W < 85$	4

Example

The masses of 30 workers in a factory are shown in the table:

$45 \leqslant W < 55$ is called a **class interval**. In this example the class intervals are all equal in width. $45 \leqslant W < 55$ means the weights are at least 45kg but less than 55kg. A weight of 55kg would be in the next class interval.

Note:
- The axes do not need to start at zero.
- The axes are labelled.
- The graph has a title.

Histogram showing masses of factory workers

When the class intervals are **not equal** in width, frequency is replaced with frequency density. See page 16.

Frequency polygons U1

A **frequency polygon** joins the **midpoints** of the tops of the bars of **class intervals** for grouped or continuous data. Consider the histogram of the factory workers again:

❶ Put a cross at the middle of the top of each bar and join up the crosses up with a ruler.

❷ You can draw a line down from the middle of the first and last bar to the x-axis to form a closed polygon, although this is not necessary.

Histogram showing masses of factory workers

Statistics and probability

Quick test

❶ Draw a pie chart for the hair colour data opposite.

Hair colour	Brown	Auburn	Blonde	Black
Frequency	8	4	6	6

❷ Use the histogram to:
   a) complete the frequency table opposite.
   b) work out how many pupils were in the survey.
   c) draw a frequency polygon.

Height (h cm)	Frequency
$140 \leqslant h < 145$	
$145 \leqslant h < 150$	10
$150 \leqslant h < 155$	
$155 \leqslant h < 160$	
$160 \leqslant h < 165$	

Histogram showing heights of year 10 pupils

Scatter graphs & correlation

Scatter graphs U1

A scatter graph (scatter diagram or scatter plot) is used to show two sets of data at the same time.

Its importance is to show the correlation (connection) between two sets of data.

Types of correlation U1

There are three types of correlation:

Positive correlation
Both variables are increasing. If the points are nearly in a straight line there is a high or strong positive correlation.

Negative correlation
One variable increases as the other decreases. If the points are nearly in a straight line there is a high or strong negative correlation.

Zero (or no) correlation
There is little or no linear relationship between the variables.

Drawing a scatter graph U1

When drawing a scatter graph:
- work out the scales first
- plot the points carefully
- each time a point is plotted, tick it off.

Example
The table shows the maths and history test results of 11 pupils.

Maths test (%)	76	79	38	42	49	75	83	82	66	61	54
History test (%)	70	36	84	70	74	42	29	33	50	56	64

The scatter graph shows that there is a strong negative correlation – in general, the better the pupils did in maths, the worse they did in history and vice versa.

Lines of best fit U1

The **line of best fit** is **the line that best fits the data points on the scatter graph**. It goes in the direction of the data and there is roughly the same number of points above the line as below it. A line of best fit can be used to make predictions. Using a line of best fit outside the plotted range may not be reliable.

For example, if Hassam was away for a maths test but got 78% in history, then from the scatter diagram you can estimate that he would have got approximately 43% in maths.

Scatter graph showing maths and history marks

Go to 78% on the history scale. Read across to the line of best fit then down.

This pupil did not fit the trend. Perhaps this student is gifted at both maths and history.

History test (%)

Maths test (%)

💡 *Do not rush when drawing a scatter graph. Plot the points very carefully. Remember to show on your graph how you made your estimates.*

💡 *It is not wise to use the line of best fit outside the group of plotted points. For example, a person who got 5% in the history test would not get 106% for maths.*

Quick test

1 Write down what type of correlation you would expect for each pair of variables.
   a) The number of pages in a magazine and the number of advertisements in the magazine.
   b) The heights of students in a year group and their marks in a maths test.
   c) The height up a mountain and the temperature.
   d) The age of a used car and its value.

Averages 1

Averages of discrete data U1

You should know three types of average: mean, median and mode.

Mean: Sometimes known as the 'average'. The symbol for the mean is $\bar{x}$.

$$\text{Mean} = \frac{\text{sum of a set of values}}{\text{the number of values used}}$$

Median: The **middle value** when the values are put in order of size.

Mode: The one that occurs the **most often**.

Range: How much the information is **spread**.

$$\text{Range} = \textbf{highest value} - \textbf{lowest value}$$

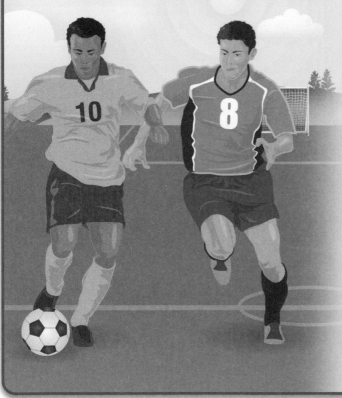

Example

A football team scored the following numbers of goals in their first 10 matches.

$$2, 4, 0, 1, 2, 2, 3, 6, 2, 4$$

Find the mean, median, mode and range of the numbers of goals scored.

- Mean $= \dfrac{2 + 4 + 0 + 1 + 2 + 2 + 3 + 6 + 2 + 4}{10}$

  $= \dfrac{26}{10} = 2.6$ goals

- Median: put the data in order of size =
  0, 1, 2, 2, 2, 2, 3, 4, 4, 6

  Cross off in pairs, from the ends, to find the middle.

  0̷ 1̷ 2̷ 2̷ (2 2) 3̷ 4̷ 4̷ 6̷

  $\dfrac{2 + 2}{2} = 2$ goals

- Mode = 2 goals because it occurs four times.
- Range = 6 − 0 = 6

> If there are two numbers in the middle, the median is halfway between them.

Check out the statistical functions on your calculator, which can be used to find the mean of a set of data.

The interquartile range U1

The **interquartile range** is found by subtracting the **lower quartile** (LQ) from the **upper quartile** (UQ).

$$\begin{array}{ccc}\text{Interquartile} \\ \text{range}\end{array} = \begin{array}{c}\text{upper} \\ \text{quartile}\end{array} - \begin{array}{c}\text{lower} \\ \text{quartile}\end{array}$$

The upper quartile is the value three quarters of the way into the distribution. The lower quartile is the value one quarter of the way into the distribution.

Finding a missing value when given the mean — U1

If you are given the mean of a set of discrete data, you can use the information to calculate a missing value.

Example

The town council wishes to make the claim, 'From January to April this year, on average 70% of rubbish has been recycled.'

The percentage of rubbish that has been recycled from January to March is:

January 72%
February 55%
March 64%

In order to make the claim, what percentage of the town's rubbish needs to be recycled in April?

Call the percentage of rubbish to be recycled in April y.

$$\frac{72 + 55 + 64 + y}{4} = 70$$

$$\frac{191 + y}{4} = 70$$

$$191 + y = 70 \times 4$$

$$191 + y = 280$$

$$y = 89\%$$

Hence, 89% of the town's rubbish needs to be recycled in order for the council to make the claim.

Finding averages from a frequency table — U1

A frequency table tells you how many data items there are in a group. For example:

Number of sisters (x)	0	1	2	3	4
Frequency (f)	4	9	3	5	2

This means 2 people had 4 sisters.

Mean $(\bar{x}) = \dfrac{\sum fx}{\sum f}$ ($\sum$ means 'the sum of')

$$= \frac{(4 \times 0) + (9 \times 1) + (3 \times 2) + (5 \times 3) + (2 \times 4)}{4 + 9 + 3 + 5 + 2}$$

$$= \frac{38}{23} = 1.7 \text{ (1 d.p.)}$$

Median Since there are 23 people who have been asked, the median will be the value in the 12th position in the table.

11 people	12th person	11 people

The 12th person has 1 sister ∴ the median = 1

The median can also be found by using the formula $\dfrac{(n + 1)}{2}$, here $\dfrac{(23 + 1)}{2} = 12$

Mode This is the data value with the highest frequency, that is 1 sister.

Range It is the range of sisters, not the range of frequencies: $4 - 0 = 4$

When finding the mean from a frequency table, remember to divide by the sum of the frequencies and not by how many groups there are.

Quick test

1. Find the mean, median, mode and range of this set of data.
   2, 9, 3, 6, 4, 4, 5, 8, 4

2. Charlotte made this table for the number of minutes students were late for registration.

Number of minutes late (x)	0	1	2	3	4
Frequency (f)	10	4	6	3	2

Calculate:
a) the mean   b) the median   c) the mode   d) the range.

Averages 2

Stem-and-leaf diagrams U1

Stem-and-leaf diagrams are used for recording and displaying information. They can also be used to find the mode, median and range of a set of data. For example, these are marks gained by some students in a mathematics exam:

24 61 55 36 42 32 60 51
38 58 55 52 47 55 55

When the information is put into a stem-and-leaf diagram it looks like this:

stem	leaf
2	4 ← Stem is 2, leaf is 4, value is 24.
3	6 2 8
4	2 7
5	5 1 8 5 2 5 5
6	1 0

Key: 2 | 4 = 24 marks

Then put the 'leaves' in order. Make sure the stem-and-leaf diagram has a key.

stem	leaf
2	4
3	2 6 ⑧ Lower quartile
4	2 7
5	1 2 5 5 5 ⑤ 8 Upper quartile
6	0 1

Key: 2 | 4 = 24 marks

See page 15 for more on lower quartile and upper quartile.

To read off the values you multiply the stem by 10 and add on the leaf. Using the stem-and-leaf diagram, the mode, median, range and interquartile range can be found easily.

Mode	= 55
Median	= 52
Range	= 61 – 24 = 37

Interquartile range = upper quartile – lower quartile
= 55 – 38
= 17

Stem-and-leaf diagrams are useful when comparing two sets of data. In these cases two diagrams are combined to make a back-to-back stem-and-leaf diagram.

The back-to-back stem-and-leaf diagram shows the masses of some boys and girls.

Girls		Boys
8 7 4 3 2 2 0	4	9
7 5 4 4 3 2 2 1 1	5	7 7 9
1 0	6	1 1 3 3 3 4 5 7 7
	7	2 3 3 5 8

Key for boys' masses: 4 | 9 = 49kg
Key for girls' masses: 8 | 4 = 48kg

Using averages and spread to compare distributions U1

Be careful when drawing conclusions from averages as they do not always tell the whole story.

For example, the lifetime of two types of battery is tested:
The mean lifetime of Trojan batteries is 9.2 hours. The mean lifetime of Warrior batteries is 11.6 hours.

From the averages, you might say that all Warrior batteries last longer than Trojan batteries. However, if you look at the range for each type of battery, you can see that this is not true:

Range of Trojan battery = 14.6 hours – 5.8 hours
= 8.8 hours

Range of Warrior battery = 13.2 hours – 9.3 hours
= 3.9 hours

Using the range, you can see that not all Warrior batteries last longer than Trojan batteries. The average lifetime of the Trojan batteries has been reduced because some of them have a particularly low lifetime.

Using appropriate averages U1

Choosing which average to use depends on the type of data you have and what you are looking for in it:
- The **mean** is useful when you need a 'typical' value. Be careful not to use the mean if there are extreme values.
- The **median** is a useful average if there are extreme values.
- The **mode** is useful when you need the most common value.

Averages of grouped data U1

When the data values are grouped into class intervals, the exact data values are not known.

When you are using grouped (continuous) data you can only find the **modal class**. This is the class interval with the highest frequency.

You can estimate the mean by using the **midpoint** of the **class** interval. The midpoint is the halfway value.

For example, the table shows the masses of some Year 9 students.

Mass (W kg)	Frequency (f)	Midpoint (x)	fx
40 ≤ W < 45	7	42.5	297.5
45 ≤ W < 50	4	47.5	190
50 ≤ W < 55	3	52.5	157.5
55 ≤ W < 60	1	57.5	57.5
	15		702.5

Adding these extra columns helps to show your working out.

(!) *Finding the mean of grouped data is a very common GCSE question and is usually worth about 4 marks.*

$$\text{Mean} = \frac{\sum fx}{\sum f}$$

$$= \frac{(7 \times 42.5) + (4 \times 47.5) + (3 \times 52.5) + (1 \times 57.5)}{7 + 4 + 3 + 1}$$

$$= \frac{702.5}{15} = 46.8\text{kg (1 d.p.)}$$

This is the same method as on page 11 except that the frequency is multiplied by the midpoint value.

Modal class is $40 \leq W < 45$

How to find the class interval containing the **median**:
$$= \tfrac{1}{2}(\sum f + 1) = \tfrac{1}{2}(15 + 1) = 8$$

The median is therefore the value in the 8th position: the 8th Year 9 student.

Mass (W kg)	Frequency	
40 ≤ W < 45	7	1st to 7th student
45 ≤ W < 50	4	8th to 11th student

The median lies in the class interval $45 \leq W < 50$.

(!) *If your calculator will do statistical calculations, particularly $\sum x$ or $\sum fx$, learn how to use it. It is much quicker, but always do it twice as a check. Always try to show full working out in order to obtain some method marks.*

Statistics and probability (side tab)

Quick test

1 The heights of some Year 10 pupils are shown in the table. 🔲

Height (h cm)	140 ≤ h < 145	145 ≤ h < 150	150 ≤ h < 155	155 ≤ h < 160	160 ≤ h < 165
Frequency	4	7	14	5	2

a) Calculate an estimate for the mean of this data.
b) Write down the modal class.
c) Write down the class interval that contains the median.

Cumulative frequency graphs

Statistics and probability

Cumulative frequency graphs | U1

Cumulative frequency graphs are very useful for finding the median and the spread of grouped data.

For example, Ahmed carried out a survey. He recorded the distances that 200 people travelled to an out-of-town shopping centre. The table opposite shows his findings.

You would follow these steps to create a cumulative frequency graph of Ahmed's data:

❶ To complete the cumulative frequency table add the frequencies, e.g. $12 + 49 = 61$.

❷ If the cumulative frequency table is correct, the final value in the cumulative frequency column should be the same as the number of people in the survey.

❸ Plot (5, 12), (10, 61), etc. on a graph. Note that the **upper class** boundaries are used.

❹ Since no people travelled a negative distance, the graph starts at (0, 0).

❺ Join the points with a smooth curve.

Distance (d miles)	Frequency
$0 \leqslant d < 5$	12
$5 \leqslant d < 10$	49
$10 \leqslant d < 15$	57
$15 \leqslant d < 20$	45
$20 \leqslant d < 25$	34
$25 \leqslant d < 30$	3

Cumulative frequency table

Distance (d miles)	Cumulative frequency
$0 \leqslant d < 5$	12
$0 \leqslant d < 10$	61 (12 + 49)
$0 \leqslant d < 15$	118 (61 + 57)
$0 \leqslant d < 20$	163 (118 + 45)
$0 \leqslant d < 25$	197 (163 + 34)
$0 \leqslant d < 30$	200 (197 + 3)

🛈 *Cumulative frequency graphs are a common topic tested on the GCSE Higher level examination. Remember to:*
- *Draw graphs as accurately as possible and try to avoid bumpy curves.*
- *Check your graph looks like an S shape.*
- *Plot the upper class boundaries.*
- *Show the method lines for the median, etc. on your graphs.*

Finding the median | U1

The **median** is the middle value of the distribution.

For Ahmed's distance data above:

Median = ½ × total cumulative frequency
= ½ × 200 = 100

Reading across from 100 to the graph and then down gives a median distance of about 13.25 miles.

Finding the interquartile range | U1

Cumulative frequency graphs can be used to find the interquartile range:

Interquartile range	=	upper quartile	–	lower quartile

Remember, the **upper quartile** is the value three quarters of the way into the distribution.
So $\frac{3}{4} \times 200 = 150$, which gives an approximate value of 18.5 miles for Ahmed's data on page 14.

The **lower quartile** is the value one quarter of the way into the distribution. So $\frac{1}{4} \times 200 = 50$, which gives an approximate value of 9 miles for Ahmed's data on page 14.

The interquartile range for Ahmed's data is 18.5 – 9 = 9.5 miles.

Using the interquartile range
A large interquartile range indicates that the 'middle half' of the data is widely spread about the median. A small interquartile range indicates that the 'middle half' of the data is concentrated about the median.

Box plots | U1

All cumulative frequency graphs tend to have the same basic shape so it is not easy to compare two or more sets of data.

A **box plot** or **box-and-whisker diagram** shows the interquartile range as a box, which makes it useful when comparing distributions.

The box plot for the cumulative frequency graph of Ahmed's data on page 14 would look like this:

Stem-and-leaf diagrams can also be used to find the interquartile range (see page 12).

Example
The times taken (in minutes) to finish an assault course are listed in order.

8, 12, (12,) 13, 15, (17,) 22, 23, (23,) 27, 29
        LQ   Median   UQ

From the data find:
a) i) the lower quartile.
    LQ = 12
  ii) the interquartile range.
    UQ – LQ = 23 – 12 = 11
b) Draw a box plot for this data.

Quick test

1 On another day Bethany also carried out the same survey as Ahmed. Her results are shown in the table.
  a) Draw a cumulative frequency graph of the grid opposite.
  b) Work out:
    i) the median for Bethany's data
    ii) the interquartile range for Bethany's data.
  c) Compare Ahmed and Bethany's results.

Distance (d miles)	Frequency
$0 \leqslant d < 5$	15
$5 \leqslant d < 10$	60
$10 \leqslant d < 15$	67
$15 \leqslant d < 20$	30
$20 \leqslant d < 25$	22
$25 \leqslant d < 30$	6

Statistics and probability

Histograms

Histograms `U1`

A **histogram** is similar to a bar chart except that it is used for continuous data and the bars can be of different widths.

In a histogram, the frequency is represented by the area of each bar, rather than its length or height.

Histograms with equal class intervals are covered on page 7. Here we will look at histograms with unequal class intervals.

Drawing histograms `U1`

When the bars have different widths the vertical axis shows the **frequency density** where:

$$\text{Frequency density} = \frac{\text{frequency}}{\text{class width}}$$

Then the **areas** of the bars are proportional to the frequencies that they represent.

$$\text{Frequency} = \text{frequency density} \times \text{class width}$$

Example
The table below shows the times, in seconds, it takes people to swim 100 metres. Draw a histogram of this information.

Time (t seconds)	Frequency
$100 < t \leq 110$	2
$110 < t \leq 140$	24
$140 < t \leq 160$	42
$160 < t \leq 200$	50
$200 < t \leq 220$	24
$220 < t \leq 300$	20

To draw a histogram you need to calculate the frequency densities. Add an extra column to the table. Draw the histogram on graph paper. Make sure that there are no gaps between the bars.

Time (t seconds)	Frequency	Frequency density
$100 < t \leq 110$	2	$2 \div 10 = 0.2$
$110 < t \leq 140$	24	$24 \div 30 = 0.8$
$140 < t \leq 160$	42	$42 \div 20 = 2.1$
$160 < t \leq 200$	50	$50 \div 40 = 1.25$
$200 < t \leq 220$	24	$24 \div 20 = 1.2$
$220 < t \leq 300$	20	$20 \div 80 = 0.25$

Interpreting histograms | U1

Sometimes you may be given a histogram and asked to use the information given in it to complete the frequency table. In order to do this it is best to find the area of each bar by using:

Frequency = frequency density × class width

Example
The histogram below gives information about the ages of some runners in a marathon. Use the information in the histogram to complete the table.

Age (A years)	Frequency
$0 \leqslant A < 20$	20
$20 \leqslant A < 30$	30
$30 \leqslant A < 40$	45
$40 \leqslant A < 60$	60
$60 \leqslant A < 100$	48

The table has been completed with the figures in red.

Using the information in the table above for this bar:
10 × 'height of bar' = 30
So the frequency density = 3
The rest of the information can then be worked out, e.g. the first bar will be 1 high, so 1 × 20 = 20, and so on.

Frequency density

Age (A years)

💡 *This is not a very difficult topic as long as you remember what frequency density is. This topic is a common one – you may be asked to interpret and complete a histogram all in one question.*

Quick test

1 Draw a histogram for the following information.

Number of hours (h)	Frequency
$0 \leqslant h < 20$	40
$20 \leqslant h < 30$	5
$30 \leqslant h < 60$	15
$60 \leqslant h < 70$	10
$70 \leqslant h < 100$	15

Statistics and probability

Probability 1

Statistics and probability

What is probability? U1

Probability is the chance or likelihood that something will happen. All probabilities lie from 0 to 1.

An event with a probability of 0.78 is more likely to happen than an event with a probability of 0.74, since 0.78 is nearer to 1.

Exhaustive events account for all possible outcomes. For example, the list HH, HT, TH, TT gives all possible outcomes when two coins are tossed simultaneously.

Mutually exclusive events are events that cannot happen at the same time. For example, if two students are chosen at random:

Event A: one student has brown hair
Event B: one student wears glasses

These are **not mutually exclusive** because brown-haired students may wear glasses.

$$\text{Probability of an event} = \frac{\text{number of ways the event can happen}}{\text{total number of possible outcomes}}$$

P(event) is a shortened way of writing the probability of an event.

Example

There are six blue, four yellow and two red beads in a bag. John chooses a bead at random. What is the probability that he chooses:

a) a red bead?

$P(\text{red}) = \frac{2}{12}$ or $\frac{1}{6}$

b) a yellow bead?

$P(\text{yellow}) = \frac{4}{12}$ or $\frac{1}{3}$

c) a blue, yellow or red bead?

$P(\text{blue, yellow or red}) = \frac{12}{12} = 1$

d) a white bead?

$P(\text{white}) = 0$

💡 *Probabilities must be written as a fraction, decimal or percentage. Probabilities can never be negative or greater than 1.*

Probability of an event not happening U1

If two outcomes of an event are **mutually exclusive**, then:

P(outcome will happen) = 1 – P(outcome will not happen)

or

P(outcome will not happen) = 1 – P(outcome will happen)

Examples

a) The probability that someone gets flu next winter is 0.42. What is the probability that they will not get flu next winter?

P(not get flu) = 1 – P(get flu)
= 1 – 0.42
= 0.58

b) The probability that it will rain on any given day in August is $\frac{3}{11}$. What is the probability that it will not rain on a given day?

P(will not rain) = 1 – P(will rain)
$= 1 - \frac{3}{11}$
$= \frac{8}{11}$

Relative frequencies U1

Relative frequencies are used to estimate probability. If it is not possible to calculate a probability, an experiment can be used to find the relative frequency.

$$\text{Relative frequency of an event} = \frac{\text{number of times event occurred}}{\text{total number of trials}}$$

Example

When a fair dice was thrown 80 times, a six came up 12 times. What is the relative frequency of getting a six?

Number of trials = 80
Number of sixes = 12
Relative frequency = $\frac{12}{80}$ = 0.15

The more trials that are carried out with an experiment, the more reliable the results.

Many trials will be needed before you can be certain that this dice is unbiased.

Expected outcome U1

The expected outcome of an event is also known as theoretical probability.

Examples

a) A fair dice is thrown 300 times. Approximately how many fives are likely to be obtained?

There are six possible outcomes and all are equally likely.

P(5) = $\frac{1}{6}$ × 300 = 50 fives

> Multiply 300 by $\frac{1}{6}$ since a 5 is expected $\frac{1}{6}$ of the time.

b) The probability of passing a driving test at the first attempt is 0.65. If there are 200 people taking their test for the first time, how many would you expect to fail the test?

P(fail) = 1 − 0.65
= 0.35
0.35 × 200 = 70 people are expected to fail

c) The probability that a mechanical component is faulty is 0.02. In a box containing 3000 of the mechanical components, approximately how many are likely to be faulty?

0.02 × 3000 = 60 mechanical components are likely to be faulty.

Quick test

1. Write down an event that will have a probability of zero.

2. A box contains three salt and vinegar, four cheese, and two bacon-flavoured packets of crisps. If a packet of crisps is chosen at random, what is the probability that it is:
   a) salt and vinegar?   b) cheese?   c) onion flavoured?

3. The probability that it will not rain tomorrow is $\frac{2}{9}$. What is the probability that it will rain tomorrow?

4. The probability of achieving a grade C in mathematics is 0.48. If 500 students sit the exam, how many would you expect to achieve a grade C?

5. When a fair dice was thrown 200 times, a five came up 47 times. What was the relative frequency of getting a five?

Probability 2

Statistics and probability

The multiplication law — U1

When two events are independent, the outcome of the second event is not affected by the outcome of the first.

If two or more events are **independent**, the probability of A and B and C…, happening together is found by **multiplying** the separate probabilities.

P(A and B and C…) = P(A) × P(B) × P(C)…

Example

The probability that it will rain on any day in August is $\frac{3}{10}$. Find the probability that:

a) it will rain on both 1 August and 3 August

$$P(\text{rain and rain}) = \frac{3}{10} \times \frac{3}{10} = \frac{9}{100}$$

b) it will rain on 9 August but not on 20 August.

$$P(\text{rain and not rain}) = \frac{3}{10} \times \frac{7}{10} = \frac{21}{100}$$

The addition law — U1

If two or more events are **mutually exclusive**, the probability of A or B or C…, happening is found by **adding** the probabilities.

P(A or B or C…) = P(A) + P(B) + P(C)… +

Example

There are 11 counters in a bag. Five of the counters are red and three of them are white.

Lucy picks a counter at random. Find the probability that Lucy's counter is either red or white.

$P(\text{red}) = \frac{5}{11}$

$P(\text{white}) = \frac{3}{11}$

$P(\text{red or white}) = P(\text{red}) + P(\text{white})$

$$= \frac{5}{11} + \frac{3}{11}$$

Red and white are mutually exclusive.

$$= \frac{8}{11}$$

Sample space diagrams — U1

When you are considering the possible outcomes of two events it can be helpful to draw a table. This kind of table is sometimes known as a sample space diagram.

Example

Two dice are thrown together and their scores are added. Draw a diagram to show all the possible outcomes. Find the probability of:

a) a score of 7

$$P(\text{score of 7}) = \frac{6}{36} = \frac{1}{6}$$

b) a score that is a multiple of 4.

$$P(\text{multiple of 4}) = \frac{9}{36} = \frac{1}{4}$$

There are 36 possible outcomes.

		First dice					
		1	**2**	**3**	**4**	**5**	**6**
	1	2	3	④	5	6	⑦
	2	3	④	5	6	⑦	⑧
Second dice	**3**	④	5	6	⑦	⑧	9
	4	5	6	⑦	⑧	9	10
	5	6	⑦	⑧	9	10	11
	6	⑦	⑧	9	10	11	⑫

Possible scores of 7   Multiples of 4

Tree diagrams U1

Tree diagrams are another way of showing the possible outcomes of two or more events. They may be written horizontally or vertically.

Example

A bag contains three red and two green counters. Two counters are taken at random from the bag.

a) Draw a tree diagram if the first counter is replaced.

| 1st counter | 2nd counter | Outcomes |

i) Find the probability of selecting two green counters.

$$P(GG) = \frac{2}{5} \times \frac{2}{5}$$
$$= \frac{4}{25}$$

ii) Find the probability of selecting one counter of either colour.

$$P(RG) \quad \text{or} \quad P(GR)$$
$$\left(\frac{3}{5} \times \frac{2}{5}\right) + \left(\frac{2}{5} \times \frac{3}{5}\right)$$
$$\frac{6}{25} + \frac{6}{25} = \frac{12}{25}$$

b) Draw a tree diagram if the first counter is not replaced.

The second event is dependent on the first event. There are only four counters remaining in the bag on the second go.

i) Find the probability of selecting two red counters

$$P(RR) = \frac{3}{5} \times \frac{2}{4}$$
$$= \frac{6}{20}$$
$$= \frac{3}{10}$$

When answering questions that involve tree diagrams, remember to:
- Make sure that on each pair of branches the probabilities add up to 1.
- Multiply along the branches.
- Add the probabilities when there is more than one alternative route, i.e. P(A or B).

Quick test

1 The probability that Meena does her homework is 0.8.
The probability that Fiona does her homework is 0.45.
Find the probability that both girls do their homework.

2 a) Draw a sample space diagram that shows the possible outcomes when two dice are thrown together and their scores are multiplied.
b) What is the probability of a score of 6?
c) What is the probability of a score of 37?

3 A bag contains three red and four blue counters. If a counter is taken out of the bag at random, its colour noted and then it is replaced, and a second counter is taken out, what is the probability of choosing one counter of each colour? (Use a tree diagram to help you.)

Practice questions

Use these questions to test your progress. Check your answers on page 110. You may wish to answer these questions on a separate piece of paper so that you can show full working out, which you will be expected to do in the exam.

Check your answers on page 110.

1 The probability that Josie gets full marks in a tables test is 0.82.
What is the probability that she does not get full marks in the tables test?

U1

2 A youth club has 75 members, of which 42 are boys. There are 15 members who are boys under 13 years old. There are 21 members who are girls aged 13 and over.
a) Complete the two-way table.

	Under 13 years old	13 years old and over	Totals
Boys			
Girls			
Total			

b) How many of the girls are under 13 years old?

3 The probability of passing a driving test is 0.7.
If 200 people take the test today, how many would you expect to fail?

4 A dice is thrown and the scores are noted.
The results are shown in this table.
Work out the mean dice score.

Dice score	1	2	3	4	5	6
Frequency	12	15	10	8	14	13

5 In a survey the heights of ten girls and their shoe sizes were measured.

Height in cm	150	157	159	161	158	164	154	152	162	168
Shoe size	3	5	$5\frac{1}{2}$	6	5	$6\frac{1}{2}$	4	$3\frac{1}{2}$	6	7

a) Draw a scatter graph to illustrate this data.
b) What type of correlation is there between height and shoe size?
c) Draw a line of best fit on your diagram.
d) From your scatter graph, estimate the height of a girl whose shoe size is $4\frac{1}{2}$
e) Explain why it is not sensible to use your line of best fit to estimate the height of a girl with size 10 feet.

Statistics and probability

6 Yusuf and Matthew are going to take a swimming test. The probability that Yusuf will pass the swimming test is 0.85. The probability that Matthew will pass the swimming test is 0.6. The two events are independent.

a) Complete the probability tree diagram.

0.85 — pass

0.6 — pass

not pass

not pass

not pass

Yusuf   Matthew

b) Work out the probability that both Yusuf and Matthew will pass the swimming test.

_____

c) Work out the probability that one of them will pass the swimming test and the other will not pass the swimming test.

_____

7 The table shows the working life of 60 batteries. Draw a histogram of this information.

Number of hours (h)	Frequency
$0 \leqslant h < 5$	9
$5 \leqslant h < 20$	15
$20 \leqslant h < 30$	18
$30 \leqslant h < 50$	10
$50 \leqslant h < 60$	8

8 A bag contains four red and three green beads. A bead is taken from the bag at random. A second bead is then taken. What is the probability that:

a) both beads are red? _____

b) the beads are different colours? _____

9 Lucy is doing a survey into whether people play sport. She decides to ask 50 people by standing outside a sports centre on a Wednesday morning. Explain why her survey will be biased.

_____

10 The box plots show the ages of males and females at a sports centre. Compare and contrast the two box plots.

_____

Males

Females

0   10   20   30   40   50   60

Age (years)

How well did you do?

0–2 Try again   3–4 Getting there   5–7 Good work   8–10 Excellent!

Types of numbers

Number

Squares and cubes `U2`

Square numbers

Any number raised to the **power 2** gives a **square number**. For example, $6^2 = 6 \times 6 = 36$ (six squared).

Square numbers include:

1	4	9	16	25	36	49	64
(1×1)	(2×2)	(3×3)	(4×4)	(5×5)	(6×6)	(7×7)	(8×8)
81	100	121	144	169	196	225	
(9×9)	(10×10)	(11×11)	(12×12)	(13×13)	(14×14)	(15×15)	

Square numbers can be illustrated by drawing squares:

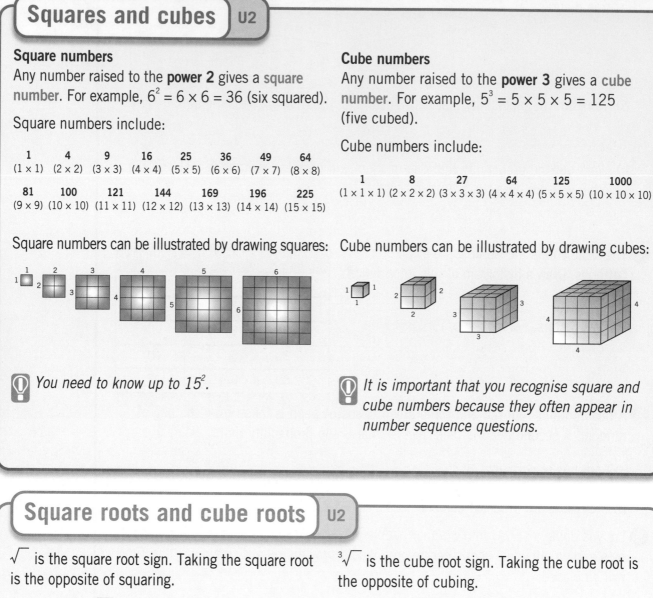

You need to know up to 15^2.

Cube numbers

Any number raised to the **power 3** gives a **cube number**. For example, $5^3 = 5 \times 5 \times 5 = 125$ (five cubed).

Cube numbers include:

1	8	27	64	125	1000
$(1 \times 1 \times 1)$	$(2 \times 2 \times 2)$	$(3 \times 3 \times 3)$	$(4 \times 4 \times 4)$	$(5 \times 5 \times 5)$	$(10 \times 10 \times 10)$

Cube numbers can be illustrated by drawing cubes:

It is important that you recognise square and cube numbers because they often appear in number sequence questions.

Square roots and cube roots `U2`

$\sqrt{}$ is the square root sign. Taking the square root is the opposite of squaring.

For example, $\sqrt{25} = \pm5$ since $5^2 = 25$, or $(-5)^2 = 25$.

$\sqrt[3]{}$ is the cube root sign. Taking the cube root is the opposite of cubing.

For example, $\sqrt[3]{8} = 2$ since $2^3 = 8$.

Multiples `U2`

Multiples are the numbers that appear in multiplication tables.

For example:
- Multiples of 3 are 3, 6, 9, 12, 15, ...
- Multiples of 8 are 8, 16, 24, 32, 40, ...

Reciprocals `U2`

The **reciprocal** of a number $\frac{a}{x}$ is $\frac{x}{a}$ $(= x \div a)$. Multiplying a number by its reciprocal always gives 1. Zero has no reciprocal, because division by zero is not defined.

For example:
- The reciprocal of $\frac{2}{3}$ is $\frac{3}{2}$
- The reciprocal of 4 is $\frac{1}{4}$ (4 is the same as $\frac{4}{1}$)
- To find the reciprocal of $1\frac{2}{3}$, first put it in the form $\frac{a}{x}$ $(1\frac{2}{3} = \frac{5}{3})$, then invert it to give $\frac{3}{5}$

Factors and primes `U2`

Factors

Factors are whole numbers that divide exactly into another number. For example, the factors of 20 are 1, 2, 4, 5, 10, 20. To find all the factors of a number, start at 1 and divide by each whole number in turn. Factors can be split up into factor pairs. For example, for the factors of 20:

```
1  2  3  4  5  6  7  8  9  10 11 12 13 14 15 16 17 18 19 20
```

So, $1 \times 20 = 20$ $2 \times 10 = 20$ $4 \times 5 = 20$

Prime numbers

A **prime number** is a number that has only two factors, 1 and itself. Note that 1 is not a prime number. The prime numbers up to 20 are 2, 3, 5, 7, 11, 13, 17 and 19.

Prime factors `U2`

Prime factors are factors that are also prime. All whole numbers can be written as products of their prime factors. For example, the diagram below shows the prime factors of 360:

1. Divide 360 by its first prime factor, 2.
2. Divide 180 by its first prime factor, 2. When 2 no longer works, try 3, then 5, and so on.
3. Keep on going until the final number is prime.
4. As a product of its prime factors, 360 can be written as:

   $2 \times 2 \times 2 \times 3 \times 3 \times 5 = 360$

   or in **index notation** (using powers):

   $2^3 \times 3^2 \times 5 = 360$

```
360 — 180 — 90 — 45 — 15 — 5
 |     |    |    |    |
 2     2    2    3    3
```

Highest common factor (HCF)

The **largest factor** that two numbers have in common is called the **HCF**.

Example

Find the HCF of 84 and 360.

1. Write the numbers as products of their prime factors and ring the common factors.

   $84\ \ =2\times2\times\ \ \ \ 3\ \ \ \ \ \ \ \ \times 7$
   $360 =2\times2\times 2 \times3\times 3 \times 5$

2. These give the HCF $= 2 \times 2 \times 3 = 12$

Least common multiple (LCM)

The **LCM** is the lowest number that is a multiple of two or more numbers.

Example

Find the LCM of 6 and 8.

1. Write the numbers as products of their prime factors.

   $8 = 2 \times 2 \times 2$
   $6 = \ \ \ \ \ \ \ \ \ \ 2 \times 3$

   8 and 6 have a common prime factor of 2. It is only counted once.

2. You take one number from each column, so the LCM of 6 and 8 is $2 \times 2 \times 2 \times 3 = 24$

Quick test

1. List the prime numbers between 10 and 30.
2. Find the HCF and LCM of 24 and 60.
3. Find a) $\sqrt{64}$ b) $\sqrt[3]{216}$
4. Write down the reciprocals of the following:

   a) $\frac{9}{12}$ b) $\frac{x}{p}$

Number

Positive & negative numbers

Integers `U1` `U2`

The **integers** are a set of whole numbers {..., -3, -2, -1, 0, 1, 2, 3, ...}.

When referring to integers, the term **integral value** is used.

A number that is **non-integral** is not an integer.

For example, the winning numbers on the lottery are:

16 **34** **49** **7** **1** **19**

When put in order they would look like:

1 **7** **16** **19** **34** **49**

Positive and negative numbers `U2`

Integers are numbers that may be **positive** or **negative**. Positive numbers are above zero; negative numbers are below zero.

NEGATIVE ← | POSITIVE →

-10 -9 -8 -7 -6 -5 -4 -3 -2 -1 0 1 2 3 4 5 6 7 8 9 10

← GETTING SMALLER | GETTING BIGGER →

For example:
-10 is smaller than -8 or $-10 < -8$
-4 is bigger than -8 or $-4 > -8$
2 is bigger than -6 or $2 > -6$

Placed in order of size, smallest first:
-7, 15, 0, -4, 6, 3, -15, 7
becomes:
-15, -7, -4, 0, 3, 6, 7, 15

Integers are often seen on the weather forecast in winter. Quite often the temperature is below 0°C.

Aberdeen is the coldest place on this forecast map at -8°C. London is 6 degrees warmer than Manchester.

-8°C Aberdeen

4°C Manchester

London
2°C

Multiplying and dividing positive and negative numbers `U2`

Multiply and divide directed numbers as normal. Then find the sign for the answer using these rules:

- Two **like** signs (both + or both –) give a positive answer.
- Two **unlike** signs (one + and the other –) give a negative answer.

For example:
$-6 \times (+4) = -24$ $-12 \div (-3) = 4$
$-6 \times (-3) = 18$ $20 \div (-4) = -5$

$(+) \times (+) = +$
$(-) \times (-) = +$
$(+) \times (-) = -$
$(-) \times (+) = -$

$(+) \div (+) = +$
$(-) \div (-) = +$
$(+) \div (-) = -$
$(-) \div (+) = -$

You need to remember the rules of multiplication/division. You will find these laws useful when multiplying out brackets in algebra.

Number

Adding and subtracting directed numbers `U2`

Number lines can help you to understand the concept of adding and subtracting positive and negative numbers.

The temperature at 6am was -5°C. By 10am it had risen 8 degrees.

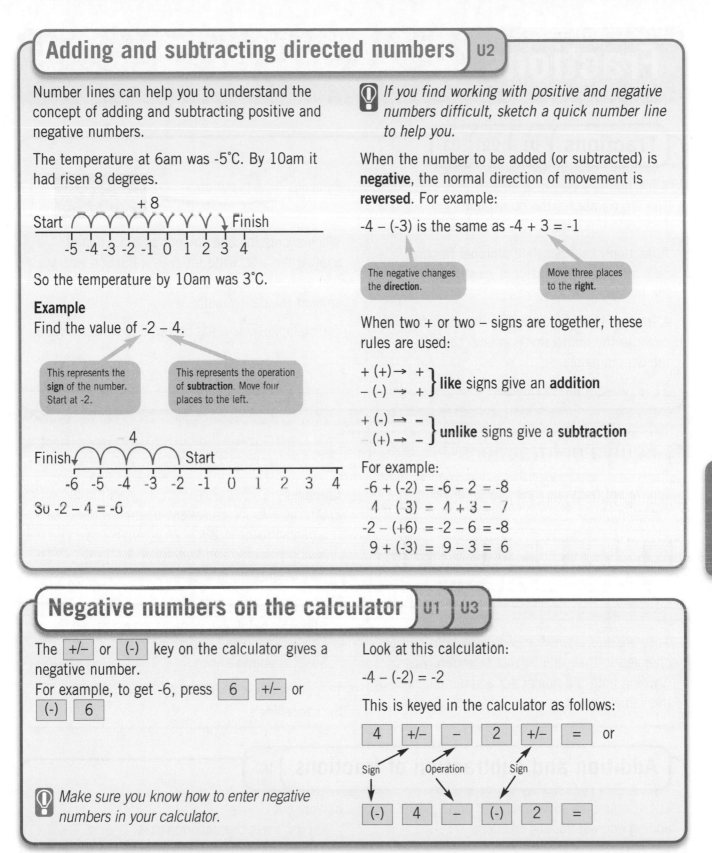

So the temperature by 10am was 3°C.

Example

Find the value of -2 – 4.

This represents the **sign** of the number. Start at -2.

This represents the operation of **subtraction**. Move four places to the left.

So -2 – 4 = -6

If you find working with positive and negative numbers difficult, sketch a quick number line to help you.

When the number to be added (or subtracted) is **negative**, the normal direction of movement is **reversed**. For example:

-4 – (-3) is the same as -4 + 3 = -1

The negative changes the **direction**.

Move three places to the **right**.

When two + or two – signs are together, these rules are used:

$$+ (+) \rightarrow +$$
$$- (-) \rightarrow +$$ } **like** signs give an **addition**

$$+ (-) \rightarrow -$$
$$- (+) \rightarrow -$$ } **unlike** signs give a **subtraction**

For example:

-6 + (-2) = -6 – 2 = -8

4 – (-3) = 4 + 3 = 7

-2 – (+6) = -2 – 6 = -8

9 + (-3) = 9 – 3 = 6

Negative numbers on the calculator `U1` `U3`

The [+/–] or [(-)] key on the calculator gives a negative number.
For example, to get -6, press [6] [+/–] or [(-)] [6]

Make sure you know how to enter negative numbers in your calculator.

Look at this calculation:

-4 – (-2) = -2

This is keyed in the calculator as follows:

[4] [+/–] [–] [2] [+/–] [=] or

Sign   Operation   Sign

[(-)] [4] [–] [(-)] [2] [=]

Quick test

1. If the temperature was -12°C at 2am, and it increased by 15 degrees by 11am, what was the temperature at 11am?

2. Without using a calculator, work out the following:
   - **a)** -2 – (-6)
   - **b)** -9 + (-7)
   - **c)** -2 × 6
   - **d)** -9 + (-3)
   - **e)** -20 ÷ (-4)
   - **f)** -18 ÷ (-3)
   - **g)** 4 – (-3)
   - **h)** -7 + (-3)
   - **i)** -9 × -4

Fractions

Fractions U1 U2 U3

A fraction is a part of a whole.
The top number is the **numerator**.
The bottom number is the **denominator**.

A fraction like $\frac{4}{5}$ is called a **proper fraction** because the denominator is greater than the numerator.

A fraction like $\frac{24}{17}$ is called an **improper fraction** because the numerator is greater than the denominator.

$2\frac{1}{2}$ is called a **mixed number**.

$\frac{4}{5}$ means 4 parts out of 5

When expressing one amount as a fraction of another amount, write them as a fraction with the first amount the numerator and the second amount the denominator.

For example, 7 as a fraction of 9 is written as $\frac{7}{9}$

Equivalent fractions U1 U2 U3

Equivalent fractions have the same value.
For example:

$\frac{1}{2}$ $\frac{2}{4}$ $\frac{3}{6}$ $\frac{4}{8}$

From the diagrams it can be seen that

$\frac{1}{2} = \frac{2}{4} = \frac{3}{6} = \frac{4}{8}$

They are equivalent fractions. Fractions can be changed to their equivalents by **multiplying** or **dividing** both the numerator and denominator by the same amount.

Examples
a) Change $\frac{5}{7}$ to its equivalent fraction with a denominator of 28.
Multiply the top and bottom by 4.
So $\frac{5}{7}$ is equivalent to $\frac{20}{28}$

$\times 4$
$\frac{5}{7} = \frac{20}{28}$
$\times 4$

b) Change $\frac{40}{60}$ to its equivalent fraction with a denominator of 3.
Divide the top and bottom by 20.
So $\frac{40}{60}$ is equivalent to $\frac{2}{3}$

$\div 20$
$\frac{40}{60} = \frac{2}{3}$
$\div 20$

This is known as **simplifying** the fraction by '**cancelling**'.

Addition and subtraction of fractions U2

These examples show the basic principles of adding and subtracting fractions.

Examples
a) Work out $\frac{1}{8} + \frac{3}{4}$
  ❶ First make the denominators the same: $\frac{3}{4}$ is **equivalent** to $\frac{6}{8}$
  ❷ Replace $\frac{3}{4}$ with $\frac{6}{8}$ to make $\frac{1}{8} + \frac{6}{8}$
  ❸ Add the numerators $1 + 6 = 7$.
    The denominator stays the same.
    So, $\frac{1}{8} + \frac{6}{8} = \frac{7}{8}$

$\times 2$
$\frac{3}{4} = \frac{6}{8}$
$\times 2$

b) Work out $\frac{9}{12} - \frac{1}{3}$
  ❶ First make the denominators the same: $\frac{1}{3}$ is equivalent to $\frac{4}{12}$
  ❷ Replace the $\frac{1}{3}$ with $\frac{4}{12}$
  ❸ Subtract the numerators but **not** the denominators. The denominator stays the same.
    So, $\frac{9}{12} - \frac{4}{12} = \frac{5}{12}$

$\times 4$
$\frac{1}{3} = \frac{4}{12}$
$\times 4$

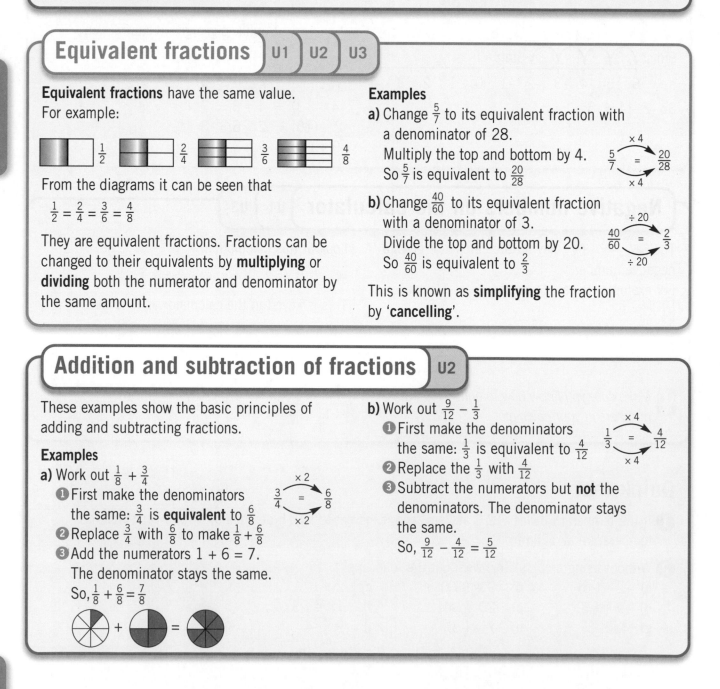

Multiplication and division of fractions 〔U1〕〔U2〕〔U3〕

When multiplying and dividing fractions, write out whole or mixed numbers as improper fractions before starting. For example:

$$1\frac{2}{9} \times \frac{4}{7} = \frac{11}{9} \times \frac{4}{7} = \frac{44}{63}$$

← Multiply numerators together.
← Multiply denominators together.

Change a division into a multiplication by turning the second fraction upside down and multiplying both fractions together; in other words, to divide by a fraction, **multiply by the reciprocal**.

Example
Work out $\frac{7}{9} \div \frac{12}{18}$
❶ Take the **reciprocal** of the **second fraction**.
❷ Multiply the fractions as normal.
So, $\frac{7}{9} \times \frac{18}{12} = \frac{126}{108}$
❸ Rewrite the answer as a mixed number.
$\frac{126}{108} = 1\frac{18}{108} = 1\frac{1}{6}$

Using the fraction key on the calculator 〔U1〕〔U3〕

$a^{b/c}$ is the fraction key on the calculator.
For example, 12 out of 18 can be written as $\frac{12}{18}$
$\frac{12}{18}$ is keyed in as 〔1〕〔2〕〔$a^{b/c}$〕〔1〕〔8〕

This is displayed as 〔12⌐18〕 or 〔12ⵑ18〕

The calculator will automatically cancel down fractions when the 〔=〕 key is pressed.

For example, $\frac{12}{18}$ becomes 〔2⌐3〕 or 〔2ⵑ3〕
This means two-thirds.

A display of 〔1⌐4⌐9〕 means $1\frac{4}{9}$. If you now press 〔shift〕 〔$a^{b/c}$〕, it converts back to an improper fraction, 〔13⌐9〕 ($\frac{13}{9}$), which means $\frac{13}{9}$

Check your calculator to see how you should enter fractions.

Proportional changes with fractions 〔U1〕〔U2〕〔U3〕

Increase and decrease
There are two methods for working out proportional changes with fractions. Use the one that is familiar to you. Remember that 'of' means multiply.

Example
Last year a gym had 290 members. This year there are $\frac{3}{5}$ more. How many members are there now?

Method 1
❶ Work out $\frac{3}{5}$ **of** 290, so $\frac{3}{5} \times 290 = 174$.
❷ Add this to the original number, so
290 + 174 = 464 people.

Method 2
Increasing by $\frac{3}{5}$ is the same as multiplying by $1\frac{3}{5}$ $(1 + \frac{3}{5})$.

On the calculator, key in

〔1〕〔$a^{b/c}$〕〔3〕〔$a^{b/c}$〕〔5〕〔×〕〔290〕〔=〕

$1\frac{3}{5} \times 290 = 464$

💡 *Make sure you know how to use your calculator to add, subtract, multiply and divide by fractions. You may need to check the instruction booklet for your particular calculator.*

Quick test

❶ Without using a calculator, work out the following:
   a) $\frac{2}{9} + \frac{3}{27}$ b) $\frac{3}{5} - \frac{1}{4}$ c) $\frac{6}{9} \times \frac{72}{104}$ d) $\frac{8}{9} \div \frac{2}{3}$

   e) $\frac{4}{7} - \frac{1}{3}$ f) $\frac{2}{7} \div 1\frac{1}{2}$ g) $\frac{7}{11} \div \frac{22}{14}$ h) $\frac{2}{9} + \frac{4}{7}$

❷ Calculate $\frac{2}{9}$ of £180.

❸ $\frac{7}{12}$ more rain fell this year than last year. If 156mm of rain fell last year, how much fell this year? 🖩

Decimals

Types of decimals U1 U2

A **decimal point** is used to separate whole number columns from fractional columns.
For example:

Decimal point

Thousands	Hundreds	Tens	Units		Tenths	Hundredths	Thousandths
8	9	2	4	•	1	6	3

The 1 means $\frac{1}{10}$, the 6 means $\frac{6}{100}$, the 3 means $\frac{3}{1000}$

Terminating and recurring decimals

A decimal that stops is called a terminating decimal. All terminating decimals can be written as a fraction. For example:

$$0.273 = \frac{273}{1000} \quad 0.49 = \frac{49}{100} \quad 0.7 = \frac{7}{10}$$

If a fraction, written in its simplest form, has a prime factor other than 2 or 5, it will convert to a recurring decimal.

A decimal that recurs is shown by placing a dot over the numbers that repeat. For example:

$$0.333... = 0.\dot{3}$$
$$0.177\,77... = 0.1\dot{7}$$
$$0.232\,323... = 0.\dot{2}\dot{3}$$
$$0.142\,857\,142\,857... = 0.\dot{1}42\,85\dot{7}$$

Decimal places U1 U2 U3

When rounding numbers to a specified number of **decimal places** (d.p.), follow these steps:
1. Look at the last number that is wanted (e.g. if rounding 12.367 to 2 d.p., look at the 6 which is in the second d.p.).
2. Look at the number to the right of it (the number that is not needed – i.e. the 7).
3. If it is **5 or more**, then **round up the last digit** that is wanted (7 is greater than 5, so round up the 6 to a 7, i.e. 12.37).
4. If it is **less than 5**, then the digit remains the **same**.

For example:
12.49 = 12.5 to 1 d.p.
8.735 = 8.74 to 2 d.p.
9.624 = 9.62 to 2 d.p.

In athletics, times are usually rounded to 2 decimal places. The men's 100m world record holder in 2009 was Usain Bolt with a time of 9.58 seconds (2 d.p.).

Ordering decimals U1 U2

When ordering decimals, follow these steps:
1. First write them all with the same number of digits after the decimal point.
2. Then compare whole numbers, digits in the tenths place, digits in the hundredths place, and so on.

Example
Arrange these numbers in order of size, smallest first:
6.21, 6.023, 6.4, 6.04, 2.71, 9.4

1. First rewrite them:
   6.210, 6.023, 6.400, 6.040, 2.710, 9.400
2. Then re-order them:
   2.710, 6.023, 6.040, 6.210, 6.400, 9.400
3. Rewrite in the original form:
   2.71, 6.023, 6.04, 6.21, 6.4, 9.4

Remember, hundredths are smaller than tenths: $\frac{10}{100} = \frac{1}{10}$ *so* $\frac{6}{100} < \frac{1}{10}$

Multiplying and dividing by numbers between 0 and 1

When **multiplying** by numbers between 0 and 1, the result is **smaller** than the starting value.

When **dividing** by numbers between 0 and 1, the result is **bigger** than the starting value.

For example:

$6 \times 0.1 = 0.6$	$6 \div 0.1 = 60$
$6 \times 0.01 = 0.06$	$6 \div 0.01 = 600$
$6 \times 0.001 = 0.006$	$6 \div 0.001 = 6000$

The results are all smaller than the starting values.

The results are all bigger than the starting values.

Calculations with decimals U2

When **adding** and **subtracting** decimals, the decimal points need to go under each other. For example:

$$27.46$$
$$7.291 +$$
$$\overline{34.751}$$

$$17.\overset{6}{\cancel{0}}\overset{9}{\cancel{0}}0$$
$$12.84 \; -$$
$$\overline{4.16}$$

Line up the digits carefully. Put the decimal points under each other. The decimal point in the answer will be in line.

When **dividing** decimals, divide as normal, placing the decimal points in line. For example:

$$\begin{array}{r} 4.8 \\ 3\overline{)14.^24} \end{array}$$

Put the decimal points in line.

A fraction can be changed into a decimal by dividing the numerator by the denominator. For example, this is how you would change $\frac{3}{5}$ into a decimal by short division.

$$\begin{array}{r} 0.6 \\ 5\overline{)3.^30} \end{array}$$

When dividing by a decimal, it is easier to multiply the numerator and denominator by a power of 10, so that it becomes equivalent to a division with a whole number. For example:

$$\frac{2.75}{0.25} = \frac{275}{25}$$

Multiply the numerator and denominator by 100.

$$= 11$$

When **multiplying** decimals, the answer must have the same number of decimal places as the total number of decimal places in the numbers that are being multiplied.

Examples

a) Work out 24.6×7

$$\begin{array}{r} 246 \\ 7 \times \\ \hline 1722 \\ {}^{3\,4} \end{array}$$

Multiply 246 by 7 – 1722, ignoring the decimal point. 24.6 has 1 number after the decimal point. The answer must have 1 decimal place (1 d.p.).

So $24.6 \times 7 = 172.2$

b) Work out 4.52×0.2

$$\begin{array}{r} 452 \\ 2 \times \\ \hline 904 \\ {}^{1} \end{array}$$

Work out 452 × 2, ignoring the decimal points. 4.52 has 2 d.p.; 0.2 has 1 d.p. So the answer must have 3 d.p.

$904 \longrightarrow 0.904$ Move the digits 3 places to the right.

So $4.52 \times 0.2 = 0.904$

c) Given that $4.28 \times 3.6 = 15.408$, find the value of:

i) 428×3.6

Multiply 4.28 by 100 to give 428, so multiply 15.408 by 100.

$$4.28 \times 3.6 = 15.408$$
So, $428 \times 3.6 = 1540.8$

ii) $154.08 \div 36$

$$154.08 \div 36 = 4.28$$

Since the numerator and denominator have both been multiplied by 10, the answer remains the same.

Number

Quick test

1 Without using a calculator, work out the following:
   a) $27.16 + 9.32$ **b)** $29.04 - 11.361$ **c)** 12.8×2.1 **d)** $49.2 \div 4$
   e) 600×0.01 **f)** 520×0.1 **g)** 20×0.02 **h)** 37×0.0001
   i) $400 \div 0.1$ **j)** $450 \div 0.01$ **k)** $470 \div 0.001$ **l)** $650 \div 0.02$

2 Round the following numbers to 2 decimal places.
   a) 7.469 **b)** 12.0372 **c)** 9.365 **d)** 10.042 **e)** 8.1794

Approximations & checking calculations

Order of operations U1 U2 U3

BIDMAS is a made-up word that helps you to remember the order in which calculations take place.

B I D M A S

Brackets
Indices
Division
Multiplication
Addition
Subtraction

BIDMAS simply means that anything in brackets is done first, then the other operations are done in the order shown.

For example:
$(2 + 4) \times 3 = 18$ but $2 + 4 \times 3 = 14$, *not* 18, because without the brackets the multiplication is done first.

Important calculator keys U1 U3

This calculator is an imaginary one to show you some of the most important keys. Make sure you are familiar with your own calculator.

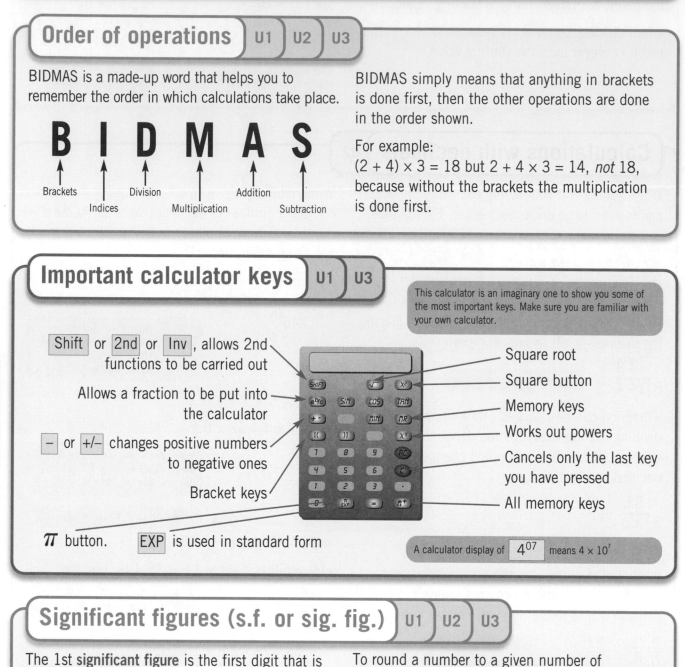

Shift or 2nd or Inv, allows 2nd functions to be carried out

Allows a fraction to be put into the calculator

− or +/− changes positive numbers to negative ones

Bracket keys

π button. EXP is used in standard form

Square root
Square button
Memory keys
Works out powers
Cancels only the last key you have pressed
All memory keys

A calculator display of 4^{07} means 4×10^7

Significant figures (s.f. or sig. fig.) U1 U2 U3

The 1st **significant figure** is the first digit that is not zero. The 2nd, 3rd, 4th, ... significant figures follow on after the 1st digit. They may or may not be zeros. For example:

6 . 4 0 2 7 has 5 s.f.

1st 2nd 3rd 4th 5th

0 . 0 0 0 4 7 0 1 has 4 s.f.

1st 2nd 3rd 4th

Take care when rounding that you do not change the place values.

To round a number to a given number of significant places, apply the same rule as with decimal places: if the next digit is 5 or more, round up. For example:

Number	to 3 s.f.	to 2 s.f.	to 1 s.f.
4.207	4.21	4.2	4
4379	4380	4400	4000
0.006209	0.00621	0.0062	0.006

After rounding the last digit, you must fill in the end zeros. For example, 4380 = 4400 to 2 s.f. (not 44).

In 2009, the tallest structure in the world was the Burj Khalifa at 828m; 800m correct to 1 s.f.

Estimates and approximations U1 U2

Estimating is a good way of checking answers. Follow these steps when estimating:

1. Round the numbers to 'easy' numbers, usually ones with 1 or 2 significant figures.
2. Work out the estimate using these easy numbers.
3. Use the symbol ≈, which means '**approximately equal to**'.
4. For multiplying or dividing, never approximate a number to zero. Use 0.1, 0.01, 0.001, etc.

For example:

$8.93 \times 25.09 \approx 9 \times 25 = 225$

$(6.29)^2 \approx 6^2 = 36$

$\dfrac{296 \times 52.1}{9.72 \times 1.14} \approx \dfrac{300 \times 50}{10 \times 1} = \dfrac{15\,000}{10} = 1500$

$0.096 \times 79.2 \approx 0.1 \times 80 = 8$

Example

Jack does the calculation $\dfrac{9.6 \times 103}{(2.9)^2}$

a) Estimate the answer to this calculation, without using a calculator.

$\dfrac{9.6 \times 103}{(2.9)^2} \approx \dfrac{10 \times 100}{3^2} = \dfrac{1000}{9} \approx \dfrac{1000}{10} = 100$

b) Jack's answer is 1175.7. Is this the right order of magnitude (about the right size)?

No. It is 10 times too big.

When adding and subtracting, very small numbers may be approximated to zero. For example:

$109.6 + 0.0002 \approx 110 + 0 = 110$

$63.87 - 0.01 \approx 64 - 0 = 64$

Questions that involve approximating are common on the non-calculator paper. For most of these questions, you are expected to round to 1 significant figure. Even if you find the calculation difficult, show your approximations to pick up method marks.

Calculations U1 U2 U3

When solving problems the answers should be rounded sensibly.

Examples

a) Jackie has £9.37. She divides it as equally as she can between 5 people. How much does each person receive?

£9.37 ÷ 5 = £1.874 = £1.87
(Round to 2 d.p. as it is money.)

When rounding remainders, consider the context of the question. For example, if the answer to a money calculation is £9.7, always write it to 2 d.p., i.e. £9.70.

b) Paint is sold in 8-litre tins. Sandra needs 27 litres of paint. How many tins must she buy?

27 ÷ 8 = 3.375 or 3 remainder 3

Sandra needs 4 tins of paint. Sandra would not have enough paint with 3 tins – she would be 3 litres short. Hence, the number of tins of paint must be rounded up.

Quick test

1. Round the following numbers to 3 significant figures (3 s.f.).
   a) 0.003786   b) 27490   c) 307250
2. Estimate the answer to $\dfrac{(29.4)^2 + 106}{2.2 \times 5.1}$
3. Sukhvinder decided to decorate her living room. The total area of the walls was 48m². If one roll of wallpaper covers 5m² of wall, how many rolls of wallpaper did Sukhvinder need?
4. Thomas earned £171.35 for working a 23-hour week. How much was he paid per hour? Check your calculation by estimating.

Number

Percentages 1

Percentages U1 U2 U3

Percentages are fractions with a denominator of 100.

% is the percentage sign.

75% means $\frac{75}{100}$ (this is also equal to $\frac{3}{4}$).

75%

Percentage of a quantity U1 U2 U3

Again, the word 'of' means **multiply**. For example, 40% of £600 becomes $\frac{40}{100} \times 600 = £240$

On the calculator, key in

| 40 | ÷ | 100 | × | 600 | = |

To work this out without a calculator, follow these steps:

① Work out 10% first by dividing by 10.
  600 ÷ 10 = £60

② Multiply by 4 to get 40%.
  4 × 60 = £240

Percentage questions appear frequently at GCSE. If there is a percentage question on the non-calculator paper Unit 2, first work out what 10% is equal to, as shown in the example above.

Example
A meal for four costs £92.20. VAT (value added tax) is charged at 17.5%.

a) How much VAT is there to pay on the meal?

17.5% of £92.20 $= \frac{17.5}{100} \times 92.20$

$= £16.14$ (to the nearest penny)

VAT = £16.14

b) What is the final price of the meal?

Price of meal = £92.20 + £16.14 = £108.34

An alternative is to use the **multiplier method**:
An increase of 17.5% is the same as multiplying by $1.175 = 1 + \frac{17.5}{100}$

£92.20 × 1.175

= £108.34 (to the nearest penny)

Percentage increase and decrease U1 U2

The answers to these questions will be a percentage, so multiply the change by 100%.

$$\text{Percentage change} = \frac{\text{change}}{\text{original}} \times 100\%$$

Examples
a) A coat costs £125. In a sale it is reduced to £85. What is the percentage reduction?

Reduction = £125 − £85 = £40

% reduction $= \frac{40}{125} \times 100\%$

$= 32\%$

b) Matthew bought a flat for £145 000. Three years later, he sold it for £162 000. What was his percentage profit?

Profit = £162 000 − £145 000
     = £17 000

% profit $= \frac{17 000}{145 000} \times 100\%$

$= 11.72\%$ (to 2 d.p.)

Hemera/Thinkstock

Number

One quantity as a percentage of another | U1 | U2

Again, to make the answer a percentage, multiply by 100%.

Fraction $\xrightarrow{\times\ 100\%}$ Percentage

Example

In a carton of milk, 6.2g of the contents are fat. If 2.5g of the fat is saturated, what percentage of the total fat content is this?

$\frac{2.5}{6.2} \times 100\% = 40.3\%$ (to 1 d.p.)

On the calculator, key in

| 2.5 | ÷ | 6.2 | × | 100 | = |

Reverse percentage problems | U1 | U2

In reverse percentage problems, the **original quantity** is calculated.

Example 1

The price of a television is reduced by 20% in the sales. It now costs £250. What was the original price?

❶ The sale price is 100% − 20% = 80% of the pre-sale price.

$\frac{80}{100} = 0.8$ (this is the multiplier).

0.8 × (original price) = £250

So, original price = $\frac{250}{0.8}$ = £312.50

$\xrightarrow{\times\ 0.8}$

original price   sale price

$\xleftarrow{\div\ 0.8}$

❷ Is the original price more than the sale price? Always check that the answer is sensible.

🛈 *It is 80% of the original price that is being found, not 80% of the new one.*

Example 2

A sofa costs £611 including VAT at 17.5%. What was the price before VAT was added?

The price is 100% + 17.5%
= 117.5% of the original price.

$\frac{117.5}{100} = 1.175$ (this is the multiplier)

1.175 × (original price) = £611

Original price = $\frac{611}{1.175}$ = £520

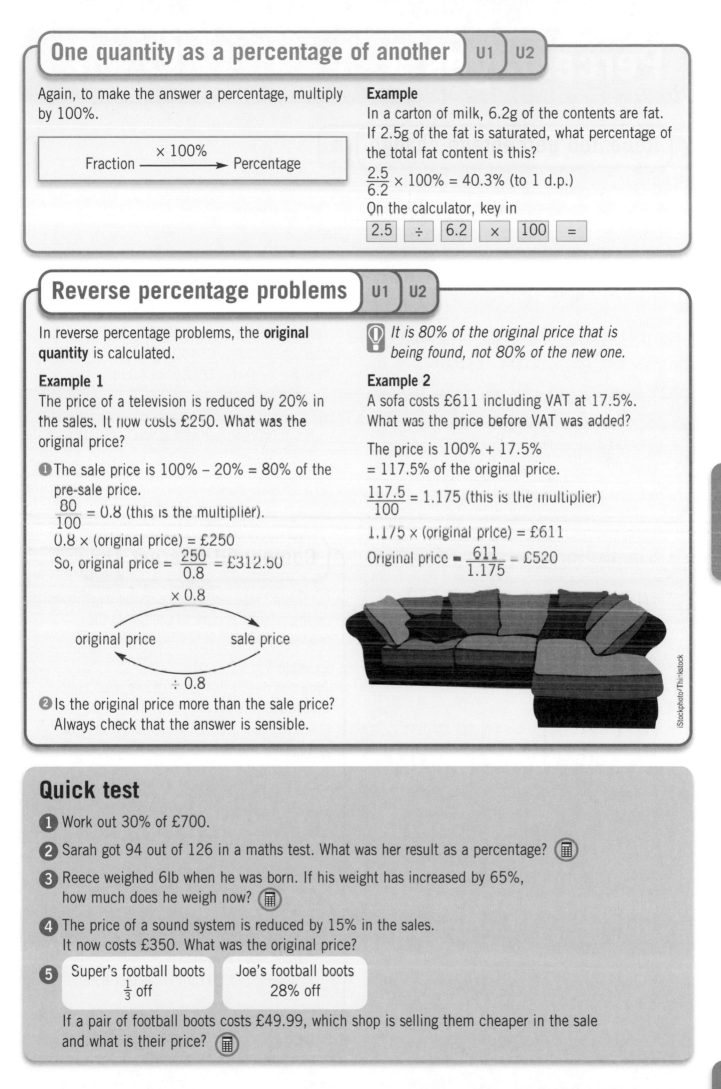

iStockphoto/Thinkstock

Quick test

❶ Work out 30% of £700.

❷ Sarah got 94 out of 126 in a maths test. What was her result as a percentage? 🖩

❸ Reece weighed 6lb when he was born. If his weight has increased by 65%, how much does he weigh now? 🖩

❹ The price of a sound system is reduced by 15% in the sales. It now costs £350. What was the original price?

❺ | Super's football boots $\frac{1}{3}$ off | Joe's football boots 28% off |

If a pair of football boots costs £49.99, which shop is selling them cheaper in the sale and what is their price? 🖩

Percentages 2

Repeated percentage change U2

The following example will help you to calculate repeated percentage change.

Example
A car was bought for £8000 in 2007. Each year it depreciated in value by 20%. What was the car worth 3 years later?

Method 1
❶ First find 80% of the original value of the car.

Year 1 $\frac{80}{100} \times £8000 = £6400$

❷ Then work out the value year by year.

Year 2 $\frac{80}{100} \times £6400 = £5120$

(£6400 depreciated in value by 20%)

Year 3 $\frac{80}{100} \times £5120 = £4096$ after 3 years

(£5120 depreciated in value by 20%)

❗ Beware! Do not do 3 × 20 = 60% reduction over 3 years!

Method 2
A quick way to work this out uses the **multiplier method**. Finding 80% of the value of the car is the same as multiplying by 0.8. The scale factor is 0.8.

Year 1   0.8 × £8000 = £6400
Year 2   0.8 × £6400 = £5120
Year 3   0.8 × £5120 = £4096

This is the same as working out
$(0.8)^3 \times 8000 = £4096$
This is a much quicker way, if you understand it!

Simple interest U2

Simple interest is the interest that is sometimes paid on money in banks and building societies. The interest is paid each year (**per annum** or **p.a.**) and is the same amount each year.

Example
Jonathan has £2500 in his savings account. **Simple interest** is paid at 5% p.a. How much does he have in his account at the end of the year?

5% of £2500

$= \frac{5}{100} \times 2500 = £125$

Total savings = 2500 + 125
                = £2625

Note: If the money was in the account for 4 years, simple interest at the end of the 4 years would be 4 × £125 = £500.

Compound interest U1

Compound interest is where banks pay interest on the interest earned as well as on the original sum.

Example
Jonathan has £2500 in his savings account. **Compound interest** is paid at 4.4% p.a. How much will he have in his account after 4 years?

Method 1
Year 1: $\frac{104.4}{100} \times £2500 = £2610$
Year 2: 1.044 × £2610 = £2724.84
Year 3: 1.044 × £2724.84 = £2844.73
Year 4: 1.044 × £2844.73 = £2969.90
Total = £2969.90 (to the nearest penny)

Method 2
Using the multiplier method:
$\frac{104.4}{100}$ = 1.044 is the multiplier
       = 2500 × (1.044)⁴
    Total = £2969.90 (to the nearest penny)

On a calculator, key in

| 2500 | × | 1.044 | x^y | 4 | = |

National Insurance

National Insurance (NI) is usually deducted from a wage as a percentage.

Example

Sue earns £1402.65 a month. National Insurance is deducted at 11%. How much NI must she pay?

$$11\% \text{ of } £1402.65 = 0.11 \times £1402.65$$
$$= £154.29$$

Income Tax

A percentage of a wage or salary is deducted as **income tax. Personal allowances** must first be deducted in order to obtain the **taxable income**.

Examples

a) Harold earns £190 per week. The first £62 is not taxable; the remainder is taxed at 20%. How much income tax does he pay each week?

$$\text{Taxable income} = £190 - £62 = £128$$
$$20\% \text{ tax} = 0.2 \times £128 = £25.60$$
$$\text{Tax per week} = £25.60$$

b) Emily earns £48 500 per year. Her personal allowance is £6475. Her income is then taxed at 20% up to £37 400 and then at 40% above £37 400. How much does Emily earn after tax?

$$\text{Taxable income} = £48 500 - £6475 = £42 025$$
$$20\% \text{ tax} = 0.2 \times £37 400 = £7480$$
$$40\% \text{ tax on } (£42 025 - £37 400) = £4625$$
$$0.4 \times 4625 = £1850$$
$$\text{Total tax} = £7480 + £1850 = £9330$$
$$\text{Earnings} = £48 500 - £9330 = £39 170$$

Being able to answer questions like the examples in this section is important – not only because they often appear on the GCSE examination paper but because they are useful in everyday situations.

There are really only two types of percentage questions:
- *'Percentage of' – here you are given the percentage, so you divide by 100.*
- *When you are asked to find a percentage. Here you need to multiply by 100.*

These questions could be on the non-calculator paper. Remember that an alternative method to the ones shown here would be to find 1% or 10% first.

Number

Quick test

1. Charlotte has £4250 in the bank. If the interest rate is 4% p.a., how much interest on the savings will she get at the end of the year?

2. A car costs £6000 cash, or can be bought by hire purchase with a 30% deposit followed by 12 monthly instalments of £365. Find:
   a) the deposit
   b) the total amount paid for the car on hire purchase.

3. A house was bought in 2007 for £175 000. The price increased by 20% in 2008 and then decreased in value by 5% in 2009. How much was the house worth at the end of 2009?

4. Fiona has £3200 in savings. If compound interest is paid at 3% p.a., how much will she have in her account after 3 years?

Fractions, decimals & percentages

Ordering fractions | U2

When ordering fractions it is useful to write them with a common denominator so that you can compare the numerators.

Example

Place these fractions in order of size, smallest first:
$\frac{1}{4}, \frac{3}{10}, \frac{5}{8}, \frac{7}{20}, \frac{27}{40}$

Since all the fractions can be written with a denominator of 40, we can compare the numerators.
$\frac{10}{40}, \frac{12}{40}, \frac{25}{40}, \frac{14}{40}, \frac{27}{40}$

In size order:
$\frac{10}{40}, \frac{12}{40}, \frac{14}{40}, \frac{25}{40}, \frac{27}{40} = \frac{1}{4}, \frac{3}{10}, \frac{7}{20}, \frac{5}{8}, \frac{27}{40}$

Fractions to decimals to percentages | U1 | U2 | U3

Equivalent fractions, decimals and percentages are all different ways of expressing the same number.

The table opposite shows:

- some common fractions and their **equivalents**, which you need to learn
- how to convert fractions to decimals to percentages.

> Get a friend to test you on the equivalences between fractions, decimals and percentages. You need to learn all the ones in the table.

Fraction	Decimal	Percentage
$\frac{1}{2}$	0.5	50%
$\frac{1}{3}$	$0.\dot{3}$	33.3%
$\frac{2}{3}$	$0.\dot{6}$	66.6%
$\frac{1}{4}$	0.25	25%
$\frac{3}{4}$ $\xrightarrow{3 \div 4}$	0.75 $\xrightarrow{\times 100\%}$	75%
$\frac{1}{5}$	0.2	20%
$\frac{1}{8}$	0.125	12.5%
$\frac{3}{8}$	0.375	37.5%
$\frac{1}{10}$	0.1	10%
$\frac{1}{100}$	0.01	1%

Ordering different types of numbers | U1 | U2 | U3

When putting a mixture of fractions, decimals and percentages in order of size, it is best to change them all to decimals first.

Example

Place the following in order of size, smallest first:
$\frac{3}{5}$, 0.65, 0.273, 27%, 62%, $\frac{4}{9}$

0.6, 0.65, 0.273, 0.27, 0.62, $0.\dot{4}$ *Put into decimals first.*

0.27, 0.273, $0.\dot{4}$, 0.6, 0.62, 0.65   *Place in order of size, smallest first.*

27%, 0.273, $\frac{4}{9}$, $\frac{3}{5}$, 62%, 0.65   *Return the numbers to their original form.*

Quick test

1. Change the following fractions into **a)** decimals **b)** percentages.
   i) $\frac{2}{7}$ ii) $\frac{3}{5}$ iii) $\frac{8}{9}$

2. Place these numbers in order of size, smallest first.
   $\frac{2}{5}$, 0.42, 0.041, $\frac{1}{3}$, 5%, 26%

Number

Recurring decimals & surds

Changing recurring decimals into fractions U2

As **recurring decimals** are rational numbers, we can change them into fractions.

Example
Change $0.\dot{1}\dot{3}$ to a fraction in its simplest form.
Let $x = 0.131313...$ ①
then $100x = 13.131313...$②
(Multiply by 10^n, where n is the length of the recurring pattern. In this example it is 2.)

❶ Subtract equation ① from equation ②.
$99x = 13$
This makes the recurring pattern disappear.

❷ Divide to leave x.
$x = \frac{13}{99}$

❸ Since 13 is a prime number, this fraction is in its simplest form.
So $0.\dot{1}\dot{3} = \frac{13}{99}$

'Trick' method
There is a quick method of changing recurring decimals into fractions – the fraction has the repeating unit on the top and the same number of nines on the bottom. For example:

$0.\dot{2} = \frac{2}{9}$ $0.\dot{4}\dot{1} = \frac{41}{99}$ $0.\dot{1}2\dot{3} = \frac{123}{999}$ $0.\dot{2}71\dot{3} = \frac{2713}{9999}$

Remember to simplify if possible. If you have a question where there are one or more numbers that are not repeated, extra care is needed.

Example
Prove that $0.2\dot{3}$ is equivalent to $\frac{7}{30}$

$x = 0.2333...$ ①
$10x = 2.3333...$ ②   Multiply by 10.
$100x = 23.3333...$ ③   Multiply by 100.
Subtract equation ② from equation ③.

$90x = 21$ $x = \frac{21}{90} = \frac{7}{30}$

Surds U2

Numbers written under a square root sign are called surds: $\sqrt{2}$, $\sqrt{3}$, $\sqrt{13}$, etc. Surds are **irrational numbers** because they cannot be written as fractions.

There are a few rules of surds that you need to learn:
- $\sqrt{a} \times \sqrt{b} = \sqrt{ab}$
  For example: $\sqrt{3} \times \sqrt{5} = \sqrt{15}$
- $\left(\sqrt{b}\right)^2 = \sqrt{b} \times \sqrt{b} = b$
  For example: $\left(\sqrt{3}\right)^2 = 3$
- $\frac{\sqrt{a}}{\sqrt{b}} = \sqrt{\frac{a}{b}}$
  For example: $\frac{\sqrt{10}}{\sqrt{2}} = \sqrt{\frac{10}{2}} = \sqrt{5}$
- $\left(a + \sqrt{b}\right)^2 = \left(a + \sqrt{b}\right)\left(a + \sqrt{b}\right)$
  $= a^2 + 2a\sqrt{b} + \left(\sqrt{b}\right)^2 = a^2 + 2a\sqrt{b} + b$
- $\left(a + \sqrt{b}\right)\left(a - \sqrt{b}\right)$
  $= a^2 - a\sqrt{b} + a\sqrt{b} - \left(\sqrt{b}\right)^2 = a^2 - b$

Examples
a) Simplify $\sqrt{200}$ Hint – look for square factors.
$\sqrt{200} = \sqrt{2} \times \sqrt{100}$
$= 10 \times \sqrt{2}$
$= 10\sqrt{2}$

b) Simplify $\left(\sqrt{2} + 3\right)\left(\sqrt{2} + 3\right)$
$= \left(\sqrt{2}\right)^2 + 3\sqrt{2} + 3\sqrt{2} + 9$
$= 2 + 6\sqrt{2} + 9$
$= 11 + 6\sqrt{2}$

c) Simplify $\frac{1}{\sqrt{5}}$
$\frac{1}{\sqrt{5}} \times \frac{\sqrt{5}}{\sqrt{5}} = \frac{\sqrt{5}}{5}$ Multiply the top and bottom by $\sqrt{5}$.
This is known as '**rationalising the denominator**'.

Quick test

❶ Change the following recurring decimals into fractions. Write them in their simplest form.
   a) $0.1\dot{5}$ b) $0.\dot{7}$ c) $0.28\dot{3}$

❷ Simplify: a) $\sqrt{75}$ b) $\sqrt{500}$ c) $\left(\sqrt{2} - 3\right)^2$ d) $6\left(\sqrt{2} + 3\right) - \sqrt{2}\left(2 + \sqrt{3}\right)$ e) $\frac{1}{\sqrt{3}}$

Ratio

Ratios U1 U2 U3

A **ratio** is used to compare two or more related quantities:

- 'Compared to' is replaced with two dots :
  For example, '16 boys compared to 20 girls' can be written as 16 : 20.
- To simplify ratios, divide both parts of the ratio by their highest common factor.
  For example, 16 : 20 = 4 : 5
  > Divide both sides by 4.

Example

Simplify the ratio 21 : 28.

21 : 28 = 3 : 4
> Divide both sides by 7.

Here is another example:

Look at the flowers shown below. The ratio of red flowers to purple flowers can be written:

$$10 : 4$$
$$= 5 : 2$$

In other words, for every 5 red flowers there are 2 purple flowers.

The ratio of 5 : 2 is the same as $\frac{5}{7} : \frac{2}{7}$

To express the ratio 5 : 2 as the ratio n : 1, divide both sides by 2:

$$\div 2 \quad \overset{5 : 2}{\underset{= 2.5 : 1}{}} \quad \div 2$$

Sharing a quantity in a given ratio U2

When sharing a quantity in a given ratio, follow these steps:

1. Add up the total parts.
2. Work out what one part is worth.
3. Work out what the other parts are worth.

Example

£20000 is shared between Ewan and Leroy in the ratio 1 : 4. How much does each receive?

1 + 4 = 5 parts

5 parts = £20000, so 1 part = $\frac{£20\,000}{5}$ = £4000

So, Ewan gets 1 × £4000 = £4000 and
Leroy gets 4 × £4000 = £16000.

Best buys U3

Use unit amounts to decide which option is the better value for money.

Example

The same brand of coffee is sold in two different-sized jars. Which jar represents the better value for money?

Find the cost per gram for both jars.

100g costs 186p so 186 ÷ 100 = 1.86p per gram.
250g costs 397p so 397 ÷ 250 = 1.588p per gram.

Since the larger jar costs less per gram, it offers the better value for money.

Number

Increasing and decreasing in a given ratio

The unitary method is useful when solving ratio problems:

❶ Divide to get one part.
❷ Multiply for each new part.

Examples

a) A photograph of length 9cm is to have its sides enlarged in the ratio 5 : 3. What is the length of the enlarged photograph?

❶ Divide 9cm by 3 to get 1 part.
  $9 \div 3 = 3$
❷ Multiply this by 5.
  $5 \times 3 = 15$cm

So the length 9cm becomes 15cm on the enlarged photograph.

9cm

3   3   3

15cm

3   3   3   3   3

b) It took 8 people 6 days to build a wall. At the same rate, how long would it take 3 people?

Time for 8 people = 6 days
Time for 1 person = $8 \times 6 = 48$ days
3 people will take $\frac{1}{3}$ of the time taken by 1 person.
So time for 3 people = $\frac{48}{3} = 16$ days

c) A recipe for 4 people needs 1600g of flour. How much flour is needed to make the recipe for 6 people?

❶ Divide 1600g by 4, so 400g for 1 person.
❷ Multiply by 6, so $6 \times 400g = 2400g$ of flour is needed for 6 people.

💡 *When answering problems of the type shown here, always try to work out what a unit (or one) is worth. You should then be able to work out what any other value is worth.*

Number

Quick test

❶ Write the following ratios in their simplest form.
   a) 12 : 15   **b)** 6 : 12   **c)** 25 : 10

❷ Three sisters share 60 sweets between them in the ratio 2 : 3 : 7. How many sweets does each sister receive?

❸ If 15 oranges cost £1.80, how much will 23 of the same oranges cost? 🖩

❹ A map is being enlarged in the ratio 12 : 7. If the length of the road was 21cm on the original map, what is the length of the road on the enlarged map? 🖩

Indices

Indices `U2`

An index (plural: indices) is sometimes known as a power.

For example:

- 6^4 is read as '6 to the power of 4'.
  It means $6 \times 6 \times 6 \times 6$.
- 2^7 is read as '2 to the power of 7'.
  It means $2 \times 2 \times 2 \times 2 \times 2 \times 2 \times 2$.

The base has to be the same when the rules of indices are applied.

$$a^b$$

The base   The index or power

Rules of indices `U2`

You need to learn these rules of indices:

- When multiplying, add the powers.
  $4^7 \times 4^3 = 4^{7+3} = 4^{10}$
- When dividing, subtract the powers.
  $6^9 \div 6^4 = 6^{9-4} = 6^5$
- When raising one power to another, multiply the powers.
  $(7^2)^4 = 7^{2 \times 4} = 7^8$
- Anything raised to the **power zero** is **1**, provided the number is not zero.
  $5^0 = 1$ $6^0 = 1$
  $2.7189^0 = 1$ $0^0 = $ undefined
- Anything to the **power 1** is **itself**.
  $15^1 = 15$ $1923^1 = 1923$

All these rules also apply when the powers are negative. These examples demonstrate some of the rules above:

- $6^{-2} \times 6^{12} = 6^{-2+12} = 6^{10}$
- $8^{-4} \times 8^{-3} = 8^{-4+-3} = 8^{-7}$
- $(6^4)^{-2} = 6^{4 \times -2} = 6^{-8}$
- $20^0 = 1$

Negative and fractional powers `U2`

Negative powers

Turn a negative power **upside down** (take the reciprocal) to make the **power positive**.

In general, $a^{-n} = \dfrac{1}{a^n}$

For example:

$4^{-2} = \dfrac{1}{4^2} = \dfrac{1}{16}$ $\left(\dfrac{2}{3}\right)^{-2} = \left(\dfrac{3}{2}\right)^2 = \dfrac{9}{4}$ $2x^{-3} = \dfrac{2}{x^3}$

Fractional powers

Fractional powers mean **roots**.

In general, $a^{\frac{1}{m}} = \sqrt[m]{a}$

So:

- the power $\frac{1}{2}$ means square root $\sqrt{}$
- the power $\frac{1}{3}$ means cube root $\sqrt[3]{}$
- the power $\frac{1}{4}$ means fourth root $\sqrt[4]{}$, etc.

For example:

$25^{\frac{1}{2}} = \sqrt{25} = 5$ $8^{\frac{1}{3}} = \sqrt[3]{8} = 2$

$81^{\frac{1}{4}} = \sqrt[4]{81} = 3$ $\left(\dfrac{1}{27}\right)^{\frac{1}{3}} = \sqrt[3]{\dfrac{1}{27}} = \dfrac{1}{3}$

Powers written as fractions

Sometimes, powers are written as fractions.

In general, $a^{\frac{n}{m}} = \left(\sqrt[m]{a}\right)^n$

For example:

$8^{\frac{2}{3}} = \left(\sqrt[3]{8}\right)^2 = 2^2 = 4$

$100^{\frac{3}{2}} = \left(\sqrt{100}\right)^3 = 10^3 = 1000$

If there is a negative fraction, remember to turn it upside down as well (take the reciprocal).

$16^{-\frac{1}{2}} = \dfrac{1}{16^{\frac{1}{2}}} = \dfrac{1}{\sqrt{16}} = \dfrac{1}{4}$

$125^{-\frac{2}{3}} = \dfrac{1}{125^{\frac{2}{3}}} = \dfrac{1}{(\sqrt[3]{125})^2} = \dfrac{1}{5^2} = \dfrac{1}{25}$

Calculating powers U1 U3

y^x or x^y or $x^\square$ is used for calculating powers such as 2^7.

Use the power key on your calculator to work out 2^7:
1. Write down the calculator keys used.
2. Check that you obtain the answer 128.

Now try writing down the keys that would be needed for the following calculations.

Check that you get the right answers.

a) $\dfrac{2.9^2 \times 3.6^3}{(4.2 + 3.7)} = 49.67$ (4 s.f.)

b) $9^{\frac{1}{3}} \times 4^5 = 2130$

c) $\dfrac{3 \times (5.2)^2}{9.6 \times (12.4)^3} = 0.004\,43$ (3 s.f.)

Quick test

1 Simplify the following:
   a) $12^4 \times 12^8$
   b) $9^{-2} \times 9^{-4}$
   c) 4^0
   d) $18^6 \div 18^{-2}$
   e) $(4^2)^5$
   f) 1^{20}

2 Simplify the following:
   a) $x^4 \times x^y$
   b) $2x^6 \times 3x^7$
   c) $12x^4 \div 3x^2$
   d) $25x^9 \div 5x^{-2}$
   e) $\dfrac{5x^6 \times 4x^9}{10x^3}$

3 Evaluate the following:
   a) $(64)^{\frac{2}{3}}$
   b) 5^{-3}
   c) $144^{\frac{1}{2}}$
   d) $36^{-\frac{1}{2}}$

4 Simplify the following:
   a) $(4x)^{-2}$
   h) $(6x^2y^4)^{-2}$

Indices and algebra U2

The rules that apply with numbers also apply to algebra.

Laws of indices

$a^n \times a^m = a^{n+m}$

$a^n \div a^m = a^{n-m}$

$(a^n)^m = a^{n \times m}$

$a^0 = 1$

$a^1 = a$

$a^{-n} = \dfrac{1}{a^n}$

$a^{\frac{1}{m}} = \sqrt[m]{a}$

Look at the following simplified expressions:

$4x^2 \times 3x^5 = 12x^7$

Note that the numbers are multiplied... ...but the powers of the same term are added.

$12x^4 \div 3x^7 = 4x^{-3}$

$(7x^2)^2 = 49x^4$

$x^0 = 1$

$(2x^4)^3 = 8x^{12}$

$\dfrac{3x^7 \times 4x^9}{6x^4} - \dfrac{12x^{16}}{6x^4} = 2x^{12}$

Work this out in two stages.

> Take care when simplifying a fraction. Work it out in two stages.

$x^6 \times 4x^3 = 4x^9$

$\dfrac{12a^2b^3}{6a^3b^2} = \dfrac{2b}{a}$

$\dfrac{4a^4b^3}{2ab} = 2a^3b^2$

$x^{-4} = \dfrac{1}{x^4}$

$x^2y^{-3} = \dfrac{x^2}{y^3}$

$(3x)^{-2} = \dfrac{1}{(3x)^2} = \dfrac{1}{9x^2}$

$(2x)^{-3} = \dfrac{1}{(2x)^3} = \dfrac{1}{8x^3}$

Standard index form

Standard index form U1 U2

Standard index form (**standard form**) is used to write very large numbers or very small numbers in a simpler way.

When written in standard form, a number will be written as:

$$a \times 10^n$$

a must be at least 1 but not greater than 10, i.e. $1 \leqslant a < 10$.

n is the power of 10 by which you multiply (if n is positive), or divide (if n is negative).

Learn these rules:

❶ The front number (a) must always be at least 1 but less than 10.

❷ The power of 10, n:
- If the number is 10 or more, n is **positive**.
- If the number is less than 1, n is **negative**.

Big numbers U1 U2

Example

Write 6 230 000 in standard form.

❶ Place the decimal point between the 6 and 2 to give 6.230 000 ($1 \leqslant 6.23 < 10$).

❷ Work out how many times you multiply by 10 to restore the number.

6 2 3 0 0 0 0   ($n = 6$)

❸ In standard form, 6 230 000 = 6.23×10^6

Other examples:
- 4371 = 4.371×10^3 in standard form.
- In June 2009, the UK national debt reached £798.8 billion, which is £798.8 $\times 10^{12}$ (a billion = 1×10^{12}). Written in standard form this is £7.988×10^{14}.

Small numbers U1 U2

Example

Write 0.003 71 in standard form.

❶ Place the decimal point between the 3 and 7 to give 3.71 ($1 \leqslant 3.71 < 10$).

❷ Work out how many times you divide the number by 10.

0 . 0 0 3 7 1   ($n = 3$)

❸ In standard form, 0.003 71 = 3.71×10^{-3}

Other examples:

0.000 047 9 = 4.79×10^{-5} in standard form.

0.0046 = 4.6×10^{-3} in standard form.

0.56 = 5.6×10^{-1} in standard form.

0.0049 = 4.9×10^{-3} in standard form.

Standard form and the calculator U1

To key a number in standard form into the calculator, use the EXP key.

(Some calculators use EE or ×10ˣ. Make sure that you check your calculator, as they all vary.)

For example, depending on the make of calculator, 6.23×10^6 could be keyed in as

| 6 | . | 2 | 3 | EXP | 6 |

4.93×10^{-5} can be keyed in as

| 4 | . | 9 | 3 | EXP | 5 | +/− |

Some calculators do not show standard form correctly on the display.

7.632^{09} means 7.632×10^9.

4.62^{-07} means 4.62×10^{-7}.

Remember to put in the '× 10' part if this has been left out.

Calculations with standard form U1 U2

You can use the calculator to do complex calculations in standard form in Unit 1.

For example:
$(2.6 \times 10^3) \times (8.9 \times 10^{12}) = 2.314 \times 10^{16}$
This would be keyed in as

| 2 | . | 6 | EXP | 3 | × | 8 | . | 9 | EXP | 1 | 2 | = |

Check that for $(1.8 \times 10^6) \div (2.7 \times 10^{-3})$
the answer is 6.7×10^8.

> Just key in as normal:
>
> | 2 | . | 7 | EXP | 3 | +/– |
>
> You should not need to use brackets

If a calculation with standard form is in Unit 2, the laws of indices can be used when multiplying and dividing numbers written in standard form.

For example:
$(2.4 \times 10^{-4}) \times (3 \times 10^7)$
$= (2.4 \times 3) \times (10^{-4} \times 10^7)$
$= 7.2 \times 10^3$

$(12.4 \times 10^{-4}) \div (4 \times 10^7)$
$= (12.4 \div 4) \times (10^{-4} \div 10^7)$
$= 3.1 \times 10^{-11}$

💡 *Watch out! Common mistakes when answering standard form questions are:*

- *Reading a calculator display, such as* 2.4^{07} *incorrectly and writing down* 2.4^7 *instead of* 2.4×10^7.
- *Forgetting to write the answer in standard form, particularly in Unit 2.*
  e.g. $(2 \times 10^6) \times (6 \times 10^3)$
  $= (2 \times 6) \times (10^6 \times 10^3)$
  $= 12 \times 10^9$
  $= 1.2 \times 10^{10}$

Examples

a) An advertising company has 6.9×10^8 active users of its website. In order to reach its target it needs to increase its active users by 15%. How many active users will need to use the website for the company to reach its target? Give your answer in standard form.

Multiplier is 100% + 15% = 1.15
Active users = $1.15 \times 6.9 \times 10^8$
$= 7.935 \times 10^8$

b) The mass of Pluto is approximately 1.29×10^{22} kg. The mass of Pluto is approximately 2.2×10^{-3} of the mass of the Earth. Work out the approximate mass of the Earth.

Mass of the Earth $= \dfrac{1.29 \times 10^{22}}{2.2 \times 10^{-3}}$

$= 5.86 \times 10^{24}$ kg (3 s.f.)

Number

Quick test

1 Write the following numbers in standard form.
a) 630 000   **b)** 2730   **c)** 0.000 042 9   **d)** 0.000 000 63

2 Without a calculator work out the following, leaving your answers in standard form.
a) $(2 \times 10^5) \times (3 \times 10^7)$ **b)** $(6.1 \times 10^{12}) \times (2 \times 10^{-4})$
c) $(8 \times 10^9) \div (2 \times 10^6)$ **d)** $(6 \times 10^8) \div (2 \times 10^{-10})$

3 Work out the following on a calculator. Give your answers to 3 s.f. 🖩
a) $\dfrac{1.279 \times 10^9}{2.94 \times 10^3}$ **b)** $(1.693 \times 10^4) \times (2.71 \times 10^{12})$

4 Calculate the following, giving your answer in standard form correct to 3 s.f. 🖩
$\dfrac{(3.72 \times 10^8) - (1.6 \times 10^4)}{3.81 \times 10^{-3}}$

Upper & lower bounds of measurement

Upper and lower bounds for a single measurement — U1

If a length x (cm) is given as 6.2, correct to the nearest millimetre, then by the usual conventions of rounding:

$$6.15 \leqslant x < 6.25$$

6.15 is called the **lower bound**.

6.25 is called the **upper bound**.

In general, the real value can be as much as half the unit above and below the rounded value.

For example, if $x = 6.23$ (correct to 2 d.p.) then the rounded unit is 0.01, so the real value can be anything between $6.225 \leqslant 6.23 < 6.235$

(See also page 77.)

Calculations with measurements — U1

When calculations are carried out using rounded values, then the calculated value lies between a maximum value and minimum possible value.

Examples

a) i) A desk measures 62cm by 95cm. Work out the lower and upper bounds of the area of the desk.

Lower bound

94.5
61.5

Lower bound of area
= $61.5 \times 94.5 = 5811.75 \text{cm}^2$

Upper bound

95.5
62.5

Upper bound of area
= $62.5 \times 95.5 = 5968.75 \text{cm}^2$

The rounded value = $62 \times 95 = 5890 \text{cm}^2$

ii) Work out the lower and upper bounds of the perimeter of the desk.

Lower bound of perimeter
= $2 \times 61.5 + 2 \times 94.5 = 312 \text{cm}$

Upper bound of perimeter
= $2 \times 62.5 + 2 \times 95.5 = 316 \text{cm}$

This is a popular topic on exam papers. You must be careful on questions with division and subtraction, as it is easy to make a mistake. If in doubt, try all the different combinations (if you have time), but don't forget to cross out the ones you don't want!

Hemera/Thinkstock

Number

b) A toy has a mass of 120g and a volume of 60cm³ (both measurements are correct to the nearest 10 units). Calculate the lower and upper bounds for the density of the toy.

The upper and lower bounds of the mass are 115g and 125g; the upper and lower bounds of the volume are 55cm³ and 65cm³.

$$\text{Density} = \frac{\text{mass}}{\text{volume}}$$

Lower bound of density $= \dfrac{115}{65} = 1.77\text{g/cm}^3$ (2 d.p.)

Upper bound of density $= \dfrac{125}{55} = 2.27\text{g/cm}^3$ (2 d.p.)

The process for working out the lower and upper bounds in multiplication and addition is quite straightforward. For subtraction and division, more care is needed. Here are a few tips:

- Finding a difference:

Upper bound $= \begin{pmatrix} \text{upper bound of} \\ \text{larger quantity} \end{pmatrix} - \begin{pmatrix} \text{lower bound of} \\ \text{smaller quantity} \end{pmatrix}$

Lower bound $= \begin{pmatrix} \text{lower bound of} \\ \text{larger quantity} \end{pmatrix} - \begin{pmatrix} \text{upper bound of} \\ \text{smaller quantity} \end{pmatrix}$

- Division:

Upper bound $= \dfrac{\text{(upper bound of quantity 1)}}{\text{(lower bound of quantity 2)}}$

Lower bound $= \dfrac{\text{(lower bound of quantity 1)}}{\text{(upper bound of quantity 2)}}$

Maximum percentage error U1

Maximum percentage error is found by using the following formula:

$$\text{Percentage error} = \frac{\text{maximum error}}{\text{nominal value}} \times 100\%$$

The 'nominal value' is the value that the quantity is supposed to have. You can think of it as the 'accurate value' (the value it would have if there were no errors).

For the desk in the example on the previous page:
Maximum error:
$5968.75 - 5890 = 78.75$
$5890 - 5811.75 = 78.25$

Therefore, the upper bound of area provides the maximum error (78.75 compared with 78.25 with the lower bound).

$$\text{Percentage error} = \frac{78.75}{5890} \times 100\% = 1.34\%$$

Calculations are not always as straightforward as this.

Quick test

1. If $x = \dfrac{4}{y}$ and $y = 6.2$ (1 d.p.), calculate the upper and lower bounds of x. 🖩

2. If $h = ab$, $a = 2.7$ (1 d.p.) and $b = 20$ (to the nearest whole number), calculate the upper and lower bounds of h. 🖩

Practice questions

Use these questions to test your progress. Check your answers on page 111. You may wish to answer these questions on a separate piece of paper so that you can show full working out, which you will be expected to do in the exam.

1 Work these out on your calculator, giving your answers to 3 s.f. 🖩　　**U1**

a) $\dfrac{4.2 \times (3.6 + 5.1)}{2 - 1.9}$　　b) $\dfrac{3.8 + 4.6}{2.9 \times 4.1}$

2 The price of a CD player has been reduced by 15% in a sale. It now costs £320. What was the original price? 🖩

3 James put £632 in a new savings account. At the end of every year interest at 4.2% is added to the amount in his savings account. Calculate the amount in James's savings account at the end of 3 years. 🖩

4 The mass of a hair is 0.000042g.

a) Write this number in standard form.

b) Calculate, in standard form, the mass of 6×10^5 hairs.

5 A television costs £320, including VAT at 17.5%. The rate of VAT is reduced to 15%. What is the price of the television now? 🖩

6 A rectangular carpet is measured as 1.42m by 1.61m.
Find the upper and the lower bounds for the area of the carpet. 🖩

7 Thomas cycles 1250m in 95s. Assuming that the time is measured to the nearest second and the distance to the nearest 10 metres, find the upper and lower bounds of Thomas' average speed in metres per second. 🖩

8 Write these numbers in standard form.　　**U1 U2**

a) 2 670 000　　　b) 4270　　　c) 0.03296　　　d) 0.027

9 The price of a television has risen from £350 to £420.　　**U2**
Work out the percentage increase in the price.

10 Mrs Patel inherits £55000. She divides the money between her children in the ratio 3 : 3 : 5. How much does the child with the largest share receive?

11 a) Express 60 as a product of its prime factors.

b) Find the lowest common multiple (LCM) of 60 and 150.

12 Fiona says the following: 'At 3pm the temperature is 4 degrees warmer than it was at midnight'. If the temperature at midnight was -2°C, what is the temperature at 3pm?

13 Show how you would estimate the answer to this expression without using a calculator. Work out the estimate. $\dfrac{8.7 + 9.02}{0.2 \times 48}$

14 Work out the answers to these questions, giving your answers in standard form.

a) $(2 \times 10^9) \times (6 \times 10^{12})$

b) $(8 \times 10^9) \div (4 \times 10^{-2})$

15 Write these recurring decimals as fractions:

a) $0.\dot{4}$ **b)** $0.\dot{2}\dot{1}$ **c)** $0.2\dot{3}\dot{4}$ **d)** $0.2\dot{7}$

16 Simplify the following:

a) $\sqrt{12}$ **b)** $\sqrt{150}$ **c)** $\sqrt{200}$ **d)** $\dfrac{6}{\sqrt{2}}$ **e)** $(\sqrt{3} + 1)^2$

17 Evaluate the following:

a) $64^{\frac{1}{3}}$ **b)** $8^{\frac{2}{3}}$ **c)** 6^{-2} **d)** $49^{\frac{1}{2}}$ **e)** $25^{-\frac{1}{2}}$ **f)** $(4)^{-2}$ **g)** $\left(\frac{5}{7}\right)^{-2}$

18 Toothpaste is sold in three different-sized tubes.
50ml = £1.24   75ml = £1.96   100ml = £2.42
Which of the tubes of toothpaste is the best value for money?
You must show full working in order to justify your answer.

(U3)

How well did you do?

| 0–4 | Try again | 5–9 | Getting there | 10–15 | Good work | 16–18 | Excellent! |

Algebra 1

Algebra

Algebraic conventions | U2 | U3

Make sure you understand the following conventions of algebra:

- A **term** is a collection of numbers, letters and brackets, all multiplied together.
- Terms are separated by + and – signs. Each term has a + or – attached to the front of it.

Invisible + sign

xy term

r term

x^2 term

Number term

- An algebraic expression must contain at least one letter (or non-numeric symbol).
- $3 \times a$ is written without the multiplication sign as $3a$.

$a + a + a = 3a$

$a \times a \times 2 = 2a^2$, not $(2a)^2$

$a \times a \times a = a^3$, not $3a$

$a \times b \times 2 = 2ab$

Collecting like terms | U2 | U3

Expressions can be simplified by collecting **like terms**. Only collect the terms if their letters and powers are identical. For example:

$4a + 2a = 6a$

$3a^2 + 6a^2 - 4a^2 = 5a^2$

$4a + 6b - 3a + 2b = a + 8b$

> Add the a terms together, then the terms with b. Remember a means $1a$.

$9a + 4b$

> Cannot be simplified since there are no like terms.

$3xy + 2yx = 5xy$

> Remember xy means the same as yx.

Formulae, expressions and substituting | U2 | U3

$p + 3$ is an **expression**.

$y = p + 3$ is a **formula**. The value of y depends on the value of p.

Replacing a letter with a number is called **substitution**. When substituting:

- write out the expressions first and then replace the letters with the values given
- pay attention to the order of operations – BIDMAS.

Examples

Using $a = 3$ and $b = -2$, find the values of these expressions:

a) $2a^2 + 4$

$$\begin{aligned}2a^2 + 4 &= 2 \times 3^2 + 4 \\ &= 2 \times 9 + 4 \\ &= 18 + 4 \\ &= 22\end{aligned}$$

> Remember to show the substitutions and the rules of BIDMAS.

b) $b^2 - 1$

$$\begin{aligned}b^2 - 1 &= (-2)^2 - 1 \\ &= (-2 \times -2) - 1 \\ &= 4 - 1 \\ &= 3\end{aligned}$$

> Be careful when substituting negative numbers.

c) $3b^3 + 2$

$$\begin{aligned}3b^3 + 2 &= 3 \times (-2)^3 + 2 \\ &= 3 \times (-8) + 2 \\ &= -24 + 2 \\ &= -22\end{aligned}$$

> $(-2)^3$ means $-2 \times -2 \times -2 = -8$

💡 *When substituting into an expression or formula, you must show each step of your working out. By showing your substitutions, you will obtain method marks even if you get the final answer wrong.*

Multiplying out brackets U2 U3

Multiplying out brackets helps to simplify algebraic expressions. The term outside the brackets multiplies each separate term inside the brackets. For example:

$3(2x + 5) = 6x + 15$

> $3 \times 2x = 6x,\ 3 \times 5 = 15$

$a(3a - 4) = 3a^2 - 4a$

$b(2a + 3b - c) = 2ab + 3b^2 - bc$

An **identity** connects expressions involving unspecified numbers. An identity always remains true, no matter what numerical values replace the letter symbols. It has a '≡' sign, e.g. $3(x + 2) \equiv 3x + 6$.

If the term outside the bracket is negative, all of the signs of the terms inside the bracket are changed when multiplying out. For example:

$-4(2x + 3) = -8x - 12$

$-2(4 - 3x) = -8 + 6x$

To simplify expressions, first expand the brackets then collect like terms.

Examples

a) Expand and simplify $2(x - 3) + x(x + 4)$
$$2(x - 3) + x(x + 4)$$
$$= 2x - 6 + x^2 + 4x$$
$$= x^2 + 6x - 6$$

> Multiply out the brackets. Collect like terms.

b) Expand and simplify $6y - 2(y - 3)$
$$6y - 2(y - 3)$$
$$= 6y - 2y + 6$$
$$= 4y + 6$$

> Take care when multiplying by a negative number.

> 💡 *If you are asked to 'expand' brackets it just means multiply them out. When you have finished multiplying out the brackets, simplify by collecting like terms in order to pick up the final mark.*

Multiplication of two brackets U2 U3

Each term in the first bracket is multiplied by each term in the second; simplify by collecting like terms.

Examples

a) Expand and simplify $(x + 2)(x + 3)$
$$= x(x + 3) + 2(x + 3)$$
$$= x^2 + 3x + 2x + 6$$
$$= x^2 + 5x + 6$$

> 💡 *When multiplying brackets like these, examiners award marks for four terms in the answers before simplifying. A common error is to think that $(a + b)^2$ means $a^2 + b^2$.*

b) Expand and simplify $(2x + 4)(3x - 2)$
$$= 2x(3x - 2) + 4(3x - 2)$$
$$= 6x^2 - 4x + 12x - 8$$
$$= 6x^2 + 8x - 8$$

c) Expand and simplify $(x + y)^2$
$$\equiv (x + y)(x + y)$$
$$\equiv x(x + y) + y(x + y)$$
$$\equiv x^2 + xy + xy + y^2$$
$$\equiv x^2 + 2xy + y^2$$

> This is an identity; it is true for all values of x.

Algebra

Quick test

① Simplify these expressions by collecting like terms.
   a) $5a + 2a + 3a$
   b) $6a - 3b + 4b + 2a$
   c) $5x - 3x + 7x - 2y + 6y$
   d) $3xy^2 - 2x^2y + 6x^2y - 8xy^2$

② If $x = 4$, find the value of:
   a) $x^2 - 4$
   b) $2x^3$
   c) $\dfrac{3x^2}{8}$

③ Multiply out the brackets and simplify where possible.
   a) $3(x + 2)$
   b) $2(x + y)$
   c) $-3(2x + 4)$
   d) $(x + 5)(x + 3)$
   e) $(y - 4)(y - 3)$
   f) $(a + 2)^2$

④ If $v = u + at$, find v if $a = -10$, $u = 25$ and $t = 4$

Algebra 2

Factorisation (putting brackets in) | U2 | U3

Factorisation is the reverse of expanding brackets. An expression is put into brackets by taking out **common factors**. For example:

$y(x + 4)$ expand $xy + 4y$

factorise

To **factorise** $xy + 4y$, follow these steps:
1. Recognise that y is a factor of each term.
2. Take out the common factor.
3. The expression is completed inside the bracket, so that the result is equivalent to $xy + 4y$ when multiplied out.

Examples
Factorise the following:
a) $5x^2 + x$
  $= x(5x + 1)$
b) $4x^2 + 8x$
  $= 4x(x + 2)$
c) $5x^3 + 15x^4$
  $= 5x^3(1 + 3x)$

Factorising can be useful when simplifying algebraic fractions.

Example
Simplify $\dfrac{5x + 15}{x + 3}$

$$\frac{5x + 15}{x + 3} = \frac{5(x + 3)^1}{(x + 3)^1} = 5$$

Factorisation of a quadratic | U2 | U3

Two brackets are obtained when a quadratic expression of the type $x^2 + bx + c$ is factorised.

These multiply to give the 2, and add to give 3 in $3x$.

$(x + 2)(x + 1)$ expand $x^2 + 3x + 2$

factorise

Examples
Factorise the following expressions.
a) $x^2 + 5x - 6$
  $= (x - 1)(x + 6)$
b) $x^2 - 6x + 8$
  $= (x - 2)(x - 4)$
c) $x^2 - 25$
  $= (x - 5)(x + 5)$

Example **c)** is known as the 'difference of two squares'. In general, $x^2 - a^2 = (x - a)(x + a)$.

Further factorising | U2 | U3

Some quadratic equations have coefficients in front of x^2 greater than 1.

Example
Factorise $12x^2 - 13x + 1$
1. Multiply the coefficient of x^2 by the constant term.
  $12 \times 1 = 12$
2. Find two numbers whose product is $+12$ and whose sum is -13.
  $-12 \times -1 = 12$
  $-12 + -1 = -13$

3. Write $-13x$ as $-12x - x$
  $12x^2 - 12x - x + 1$
4. Factorise by grouping; the bracketed term must be the same.
  $12x(x - 1) - 1(x - 1)$
5. $(x - 1)$ is a common factor.
  $(x - 1)(12x - 1)$

Hence: $12x^2 - 13x + 1 = (x - 1)(12x - 1)$

When working with algebraic fractions, the rules are the same as for ordinary fractions.

Addition and subtraction

Always find a common denominator (the same bottom line) and then correct the numerators. Simplify by multiplying out the numerator and collecting like terms. For example:

$$\frac{x+2}{x-1} + \frac{3}{x}$$

$$= \frac{x(x+2)}{x(x-1)} + \frac{3(x-1)}{x(x-1)}$$

$$= \frac{x^2 + 2x + 3x - 3}{x(x-1)}$$

$$= \frac{x^2 + 5x - 3}{x(x-1)}$$

$$\frac{5}{(x+2)} - \frac{2}{(x-3)}$$

$$= \frac{5(x-3) - 2(x+2)}{(x+2)(x-3)}$$

$$= \frac{5x - 15 - 2x - 4}{(x+2)(x-3)}$$

$$= \frac{3x - 19}{(x+2)(x-3)}$$

Multiplication

Simply multiply the numerators together and the denominators together and cancel if possible. For example:

$$\frac{3p^2q}{r^2s} \times \frac{2rs}{9pq^2}$$

$$= \frac{2p}{3qr}$$

Division

Remember to turn the second fraction upside down (i.e. take the reciprocal), then multiply and cancel if possible. For example:

$$\frac{6(x+2)}{(x-1)} \div \frac{12(x+2)(x+3)}{(x+1)}$$

$$= \frac{6(x+2)}{(x-1)} \times \frac{(x+1)}{12(x+2)(x+3)}$$

$$= \frac{(x+1)}{2(x-1)(x+3)}$$

Algebra

Quick test

1 Factorise the following expressions.

a) $3x + 9$ b) $5y - 15$

c) $12x^2 - 6x$ d) $x^2 - 5x - 6$

e) $x^2 - 3x + 2$ f) $x^2 - 16$

g) $2x^2 - 7x + 3$ h) $6x^2 + 5x + 1$

2 Simplify the following algebraic fractions.

a) $\dfrac{2}{(x+2)} + \dfrac{3}{(x-1)}$

b) $\dfrac{4(s-1)}{3(s+2)} \times \dfrac{(s+2)^2}{8(s-3)}$

c) $\dfrac{8(a^2 - b^2)}{3(a+2)} \div \dfrac{4(a-b)}{27(a+1)}$

Equations 1

Solving linear equations of the form $ax + b = cx + d$ U2 U3

An equation involves finding at least one unknown value that has to be worked out.

The trick with linear equations is to get all the x terms together on one side of the equals sign and the numbers on the other side.

Example

Solve $5x - 9 = 12 - 4x$

$$9x - 9 = 12$$ ← Add $4x$ to both sides.
$$9x = 21$$ ← Add 9 to both sides.
$$x = \tfrac{21}{9} = 2\tfrac{1}{3}$$

If in the exam you do not know that $\tfrac{21}{9} = 2\tfrac{1}{3}$, leave it as $\tfrac{21}{9}$ to obtain full marks.

Solving linear equations with brackets U2 U3

Just because an equation has brackets, don't be put off. The method is just the same as for the other equations once the brackets have been multiplied out.

Examples

a) Solve $3(x - 2) = 2(x + 6)$

$$3x - 6 = 2x + 12$$ ← Multiply out the brackets first.
$$x - 6 = 12$$
$$x = 18$$

b) Solve $5(x - 2) + 6 = 3(x - 4) + 10$

$$5x - 10 + 6 = 3x - 12 + 10$$
$$5x - 4 = 3x - 2$$
$$2x = 2$$
$$x = 1$$

Solving quadratic equations U2 U3

Make sure the quadratic equation is equal to zero. Then factorise the quadratic equation.

Examples

a) Solve $x^2 - 5x = 0$ x is a common factor.

$$x(x - 5) = 0$$
Either $x = 0$,
or $x - 5 = 0$, i.e. $x = 5$.

b) Solve $x^2 - 3x = 10$

$$x^2 - 3x - 10 = 0$$ Make it equal to zero, then factorise.
$$(x + 2)(x - 5) = 0$$
Either $(x + 2) = 0$, i.e. $x = -2$,
or $(x - 5) = 0$, i.e. $x = 5$.

c) Solve $3x^2 - x - 4 = 0$ Product: $3 \times -4 = -12$
Sum: $3 + -4 = -1$

$$3x^2 + 3x - 4x - 4 = 0$$
$$3x(x + 1) - 4(x + 1) = 0$$
$$(x + 1)(3x - 4) = 0$$
Either $x + 1 = 0$, i.e. $x = -1$,
or $3x - 4 = 0$, i.e. $x = \tfrac{4}{3}$

Algebra

Completing the square U2 U3

Completing the square is the method used when quadratic equations are expressed in the form $(x + a)^2 + b = 0$. Follow these steps:

1. Rearrange the equation in the form $ax^2 + bx + c = 0$. If a is not 1, then divide the whole equation by a.
2. Write the equation in the form $(x + \frac{b}{2})^2$ Notice that the constant in the bracket is always half the value of b!
3. Multiply out the brackets, compare to the original and adjust by adding or subtracting an extra amount.

The minimum value of $(x + a)^2 + b$ occurs at b since $(x + a)^2 \geqslant 0$.

Example

Express $x^2 - 4x + 1 = 0$ as a completed square and, hence, solve it.

1. $x^2 - 4x + 1 = 0$

   > This is already in the form $ax^2 + bx + c = 0$ and $a = 1$.

2. $(x - 2)^2$

   > Half of -4 is -2.

3. $(x - 2)^2 = x^2 - 4x + 4$

   > Multiply out the brackets and now compare to the original $x^2 - 4x + 1$. To make $x^2 - 4x + 4$ like the original we need to subtract 3. Now we need to solve the equation.

4. So $(x - 2)^2 - 3 = 0$

   $(x - 2)^2 = 3$

   $(x - 2) = \pm \sqrt{3}$

   > Leave your answer in surd form.

   So $x = \sqrt{3} + 2$, or $x = -\sqrt{3} + 2$

Using equations to solve problems U2 U3

The following example will help you to understand how equations can be used to solve problems.

Example

The perimeter of the triangle is 20cm.
Work out the value of x and hence find the length of the three sides.

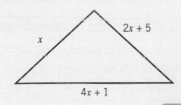

$x + (2x + 5) + (4x + 1) = 20$

$7x + 6 = 20$

$7x = 20 - 6$

$7x = 14$

$x = \frac{14}{7} = 2$

> The perimeter is found by adding the lengths together. Collect like terms and solve the equation as before.

So the lengths of the sides are
2 (= x), 9 (= $2x + 5$) and 9 (= $4x + 1$).

> Solving equations is a very common topic at GCSE. Try to work through them in a logical way, always showing full working out. If you have time, check your answer by substituting it back into the equation to see if it works.

Quick test

1. Solve the following equations.

   a) $2x - 3 = 9$

   b) $4x + 2 = 20$

   c) $5x + 3 = 2x + 9$

   d) $6x - 1 = 15 + 2x$

   e) $3(x + 2) = x + 4$

   f) $2(x - 1) = 12(x + 1)$

   g) $x^2 + 4x - 5 = 0$

   h) $x^2 - 5x + 6 = 0$

   i) $3x^2 - 7x + 2 = 0$

   j) $2x^2 + 5x + 2 = 0$

Equations 2

Simultaneous equations U2

Two equations with two unknowns are called simultaneous equations. They can be solved in several ways. Solving equations simultaneously involves finding values for the letters that will make both equations work.

Graphical method

The points at which any two graphs intersect represent the simultaneous solutions of those equations.

Example

Solve the simultaneous equations
$y = 2x - 1$ and $x + y = 5$.

❶ Draw the two graphs.

$y = 2x - 1$	If $x = 0$, $y = -1$
	If $y = 0$, $x = \frac{1}{2}$
$x + y = 5$	If $x = 0$, $y = 5$
	If $x = 5$, $y = 0$

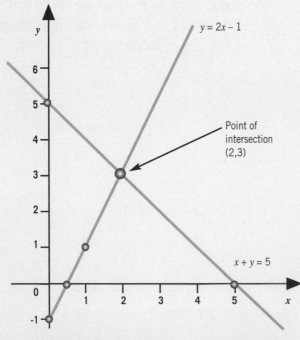

Point of intersection (2,3)

❷ At the point of intersection $x = 2$ and $y = 3$.

Elimination method

If the coefficient of one of the letters is the same in both equations, then that letter may be eliminated by subtracting the equations.

The coefficient is the number a letter is multiplied by, e.g. the coefficient of $-2x$ is -2.

Example

Solve simultaneously $2x + 3y = 6$ and $x + y = 1$.

❶ Label the equations ① and ②.

$$2x + 3y = 6 \quad ①$$
$$x + y = 1 \quad ②$$

❷ Since no coefficients match, multiply equation ② by 2. Rename it equation ③.

$$\left.\begin{array}{l} 2x + 3y = 6 \quad ① \\ 2x + 2y = 2 \quad ③ \end{array}\right\} \times 2$$

❸ The coefficients of x in equations ① and ③ are the same. Subtract equation ③ from equation ① and then solve the remaining equation.

$$2x + 3y = 6$$
$$\underline{2x + 2y = 2}$$
$$0x + y = 4$$
$$\therefore y = 4$$

❹ Substitute the value $y = 4$ into equation ① or equation ②. Solve the resulting equation to find x.

$$x + 4 = 1$$
$$x = 1 - 4$$
$$x = -3$$

❺ Check in equation ①.

$$(2 \times -3) + (3 \times 4) = 6$$
$$-6 + 12 = 6 ✔$$

The solution is $x = -3$, $y = 4$

💡 *Simultaneous equations can be difficult to master. Try to learn the steps outlined here and practise lots of examples. Use the check at the end to make sure that you have the correct answers.*

💡 *Remember:*
- *to eliminate terms with opposite signs, add the equations*
- *to eliminate terms with the same signs, subtract the equations.*

Algebra

Trial and improvement gives an approximate solution to **cubic equations** and other equations that cannot be solved using algebra.

Example

The equation $x^3 - 5x = 10$ has a solution between 2 and 3. Find this solution to 2 decimal places.

Draw a table to help.
Substitute different values of x into $x^3 - 5x$.

x	$x^3 - 5x$	Comment
2.5	3.125	too small
2.8	7.952	too small
2.9	9.889	too small
2.95	10.922375	too big
2.94	10.712184	too big
2.91	10.092171	too big

At this stage the solution is 'trapped' between 2.90 and 2.91. Checking the middle value, $x = 2.905$, gives $x^3 - 5x = 9.99036...$ which is too small.

| 2.90 | 2.905 | 2.91 |
| (too small) | (too small) | (too big) |

Because $x = 2.905$ is too small, the solution is $x = 2.91$ correct to 2 decimal places.

🔘 *Make sure you write down the solution of x, not the answer to $x^3 - 5x$.*

Quick test

1. Solve the following pairs of simultaneous equations.
   a) $4x + 7y = 10$
      $2x + 3y = 3$
   b) $3a - 5b = 1$ ①   Hint – multiply equation ① by 2 and equation ② by 3.
      $2a + 3b = 7$ ②

2. The diagram shows the graphs of the equations $x + y = 2$ and $y = x - 4$.

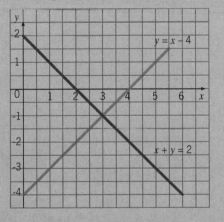

   Use the diagram to solve the simultaneous equations
   $x + y = 2$
   $y = x - 4$

3. The equation $y^3 + y = 40$ has a solution between 3 and 4.
   Find this solution to 1 d.p. by using a method of trial and improvement. 🖩

Number patterns & sequences

Sequences U2

A **sequence** is a list of numbers. There is usually a relationship between the numbers. Each number in the list is called a **term**.

For example, the odd numbers form a sequence 1, 3, 5, 7, 9, 11, ..., in which the terms have a **common difference** of 2.

1 \ 3 \ 5 \ 7 \ 9 \ 11...
  2 2 2 2 2

Important number sequences

Square numbers:	1, 4, 9, 16, 25, ...
Cube numbers:	1, 8, 27, 64, 125, ...
Powers of 2:	1, 2, 4, 8, 16, ...
Triangular numbers:	1, 3, 6, 10, 15, ...
The Fibonacci sequence:	1, 1, 2, 3, 5, 8, 13, ...
Powers of 10:	1, 10, 100, 1000, ...

Finding the nth term of a linear sequence U2

The nth term gives an expression for the term in the nth position.

The nth term of a sequence is more efficient as it allows any term in a sequence to be found without relying on knowing the previous term.

The nth term of a linear sequence is of the form $an + b$.

If the numbers in the sequence are decreasing then the coefficient of n will always be negative.

Examples
a) Find an expression for the nth term of this sequence: 3, 5, 7, 9...

  ① Find the common difference; this is **a**.

    3 \ 5 \ 7 \ 9
      2 2 2

  Difference = 2, so **a** = 2.
  So the nth term = $2n + b$

Term	1	2	3	4	............n
Number in sequence	3	5	7	9	....

② Now substitute the value of $n = 1$ and the number in the sequence, in this case it is 3.

nth term = $2n + b$
$$3 = 2 \times 1 + b$$
$$3 = 2 + b$$
$$3 - 2 = b$$
$$b = 1$$

nth term is $2n + 1$

③ Check when $n = 2$ $2 \times 2 + 1 = 5$
Number in sequence is 5 so the nth term is $2n + 1$.

b) In a fairground game, a prize is won if the number you pick out of a jar is in the sequence whose nth term is $3n - 4$. Josie picks a card with the number 600. Explain whether Josie wins a prize.

$$3n - 4 = 600$$
$$3n = 600 + 4$$
$$3n = 604$$

Since 604 is not a multiple of 3, Josie does not win a prize.

Quick test

① Write down the next two terms in each of these sequences.
  a) 5, 7, 9, 11, ___ , ___ **b)** 1, 4, 9, 16, ___ , ___ **c)** 12, 10, 8, 6, ___ , ___

② Write down the nth term of each of these sequences.
  a) 5, 7, 9, 11, ... **b)** 2, 5, 8, 11, ... **c)** 6, 10, 14, 18, ... **d)** 8, 6, 4, 2, ...

Algebra

Inequalities

The four inequality symbols U2

Inequalities are solved in a similar way to equations.

> means 'greater than'
< means 'less than'
≥ means 'greater than or equal to'
≤ means 'less than or equal to'

So $x > 3$ and $3 < x$ both say 'x is greater than 3'.

Dividing by a negative number reverses the direction of the inequality sign:

$$-2x < 6$$
$$x > \frac{6}{-2}$$
$$x > -3$$

Examples
Solve the following inequalities.

a) $2x + 1 < 11$

$$2x < 11 - 1$$
$$2x < 10$$
$$x < \frac{10}{2}$$
$$x < 5$$

The solution of this inequality can be represented on a number line:

This circle is open

5

b) $4x - 2 < 2x + 6$

$$2x - 2 < 6$$ ← Subtract $2x$ from both sides.
$$2x < 8$$ ← Add 2 to both sides.
$$x < 4$$ ← Divide both sides by 2.

This circle is open

4

c) $-5 < 3x + 1 \leqslant 13$

$$-6 < 3x \leqslant 12$$ ← Subtract 1 from each side.
$$-2 < x \leqslant 4$$ ← Divide each side by 3.

The **integer values** that satisfy this inequality are -1, 0, 1, 2, 3, 4, which can be represented on a number line:

-2 -1 0 1 2 3 4

Use ● when the end point is included and ○ when the end point is not included.

Graphs of inequalities U2

The graph of an equation such as $y = 3$ is a line, whereas the graph of the inequality $y < 3$ is a **region** that has the line $y = 3$ as its **boundary**.

To show the region for given inequalities you need to:

- Draw the boundary lines first.
- It is often easier with several inequalities to shade out the unwanted regions, so that the solution is shown **unshaded** (as in the example).

For example,
the diagram shows unshaded the region $x > 1$, $x + y \leqslant 4$, $y \geqslant 0$

Graphical inequalities are used in an area of mathematics called linear programming. Linear programming is used for solving allocation problems and is widely used in businesses and organisations.

Quick test

1 Solve the following inequalities:

a) $2x - 3 < 9$ b) $5x + 1 \geqslant 21$ c) $1 \leqslant 3x - 2 \leqslant 7$ d) $1 \leqslant 5x + 2 < 12$

Formulae

Writing formulae U2 U3

You need to be able to write a formula when given some information or a diagram.

Examples

a) Frances buys x books at £2.50 each. She pays with a £20 note. If she receives C pounds change, write down a formula for C.

$$C = 20 - 2.50x$$

Notice that no £ signs are put in the formula.

This is the amount of money she spent.

If in doubt, check by substituting a value for x, e.g. if she bought 2 books $x = 2$, so her change would be $20 - 2.50 \times 2 = £15$ ✔

b) Some patterns are made by using grey and white paving slabs.

i) Write a formula for the number of grey paving slabs (g) in a pattern that uses w white ones.

The formula is $g = 2w + 2$

2w represents the 2 layers

+ 2 gives the grey slabs on either end of the white ones.

ii) Andy builds a patio using the pattern shown above. He uses 24 white slabs. How many grey slabs will he need to buy?

$g = 2w + 2$
$g = 2 \times 24 + 2$
$g = 48 + 2$
$g = 50$

Andy needs to buy 50 grey slabs.

Using formulae U2 U3

A formula describes the relationship between two (or more) variables. A formula must have an equals sign (=) in it.

Examples

a) Thomas hires a van. There is a standing charge of £17 and then it costs £21 per day.

How much does it cost for:
i) 6 days?
$17 + (21 \times 6) = £143$
ii) y days?
$17 + (21 \times y) = £(17 + 21y)$
iii) Write a formula for the total hire cost C.
$C = 17 + 21y$ This is a formula that works out the cost of hiring the van for any number of days.

b) A rule for working out the average carbon dioxide emission from a coach is given by:

$$\text{Carbon dioxide emission} = \frac{\text{Distance travelled (km)}}{\times 0.17}$$

If C stands for the carbon dioxide emission in grams and d stands for the distance travelled in kilometres:
i) write down a formula for the total carbon dioxide emission, C.
$C = d \times 0.17$ or $C = 0.17d$

ii) work out the carbon dioxide emission for a coach that travels a distance of 28km.
$C = 28 \times 0.17$
$= 4.76$ grams

Algebra

Substituting into formulae [U2] [U3]

Substituting into formulae is similar to substituting into expressions. Replacing a letter with a number is called **substitution**. When substituting:
- replace the letters in the formula with the value given
- if in Unit 2, work out systematically, taking care with negatives
- if in Unit 3, work out the value on your calculator. Use bracket keys where possible and pay attention to the order of operations.

Example
The formula $C = \dfrac{5(F - 32)}{9}$ is used to change the temperature from degrees Fahrenheit into degrees centigrade. Work out the value of C when $F = -12$.

$$C = \frac{5(-12 - 32)}{9}$$
> Substitute the value of F into the formula.

$$C = \frac{5 \times (-44)}{9}$$
> Work out the brackets first, then multiply by $\frac{5}{9}$.

$$C = -24.\dot{4}°C \text{ or } -24\tfrac{4}{9}°C$$

Rearranging formulae [U2]

The **subject of a formula** is the letter that appears on its own on one side of the formula.

Examples
Make p the subject of these formulae:

a) $r = (p + 6)^2$

$r = (p + 6)^2$
> Deal with the power first. Take the square root of both sides.

$\pm\sqrt{r} = p + 6$
> Remove any terms added or subtracted. So subtract 6 from both sides.

$\pm\sqrt{r} - 6 = p$ **or** $p = \pm\sqrt{r} - 6$
> The subject of the formula is usually written first.

b) $y = \dfrac{p + r}{6}$

$y = \dfrac{p + r}{6}$
> First deal with the term dividing p; multiply both sides by 6.

$6y = p + r$
> Remove r by subtracting r from both sides.

$6y - r = p$ **or** $p = 6y - r$

The following example will help you to understand how to rearrange formulae when the subject appears in more than one term.

Example
Make y the subject of the formula $a = \dfrac{y + b}{y - c}$

$$a = \frac{y + b}{y - c}$$
$$a(y - c) = y + b$$
> Multiply both sides by $(y - c)$.
$$ay - ac = y + b$$
> Multiply out the brackets.
$$ay - y = b + ac$$
> Collect the terms involving y on one side of the equation.
$$y(a - 1) = b + ac$$
> Factorise.

So $$y = \frac{b + ac}{a - 1}$$

> *Practise plenty of questions on this topic to help you become confident when working with more complex algebra. GCSE questions on this topic usually carry a lot of marks.*

Quick test

1. Using $p = 6.2$, $r = -3.2$ and $s = 3$, find the value of A in each of the following formulae, giving your answers to 3 s.f.
   a) $A = pr + s$ **b)** $A = p^2s - r$ **c)** $A = r^2 - \dfrac{p}{s}$ **d)** $A = (ps - r)^2$

2. Make u the subject of the formula $v^2 = u^2 + 2as$

3. $V = IR$. Make R the subject of the formula.

4. Make r the subject of the formula $p = \dfrac{r - y}{r + s}$

The quadratic formula

The quadratic formula U3

If a quadratic equation of the form $ax^2 + bx + c = 0$ cannot be solved by factorisation or completing the square (see pages 52–55), the following quadratic formula can be used:

$$x = \frac{-b \pm \sqrt{b^2 - 4ac}}{2a}$$

This formula can be used for any quadratic equation written in the form $ax^2 + bx + c = 0$.

Examples

a) Find the solutions of $2x^2 + x = 7$ to 2 decimal places.

❶ Put the equation into the form $ax^2 + bx + c = 0$ hence $2x^2 + x - 7 = 0$

❷ Identify the values of a, b and c:
$a = 2, b = 1, c = -7$

❸ Substitute these values into the quadratic formula:

$$x = \frac{-b \pm \sqrt{b^2 - 4ac}}{2a}$$

$$x = \frac{-1 \pm \sqrt{1^2 - (4 \times 2 \times -7)}}{2 \times 2} = \frac{-1 \pm \sqrt{1 + 56}}{4}$$

$$= \frac{-1 \pm \sqrt{57}}{4}$$

| One solution is when we use $-\sqrt{57}$: | $x = \dfrac{-1 - \sqrt{57}}{4} = -2.14$ |

| The other solution is when we use $+\sqrt{57}$: | $x = \dfrac{-1 + \sqrt{57}}{4} = 1.64$ |

❹ To check, put these values into the original equation.

$2 \times (-2.14)^2 + (-2.14) = 7$ ✓

$2 \times (1.64)^2 + (1.64) = 7$ ✓

b) The diagram shows a trapezium. The measurements are in centimetres and the area of the trapezium is 85cm². Work out the height of the trapezium, giving your answer to 2 decimal places.

❶ The formula for the area of a trapezium is $A = \frac{1}{2}(a + b) \times h$

❷ Substituting the values above gives
$85 = \frac{1}{2} \times (x + 20) \times 3x$

❸ Multiply by 2: $170 = 3x (x + 20)$

❹ Multiply out the brackets: $170 = 3x^2 + 60x$

❺ Rearrange into the form $ax^2 + bx + c = 0$, then solve using the quadratic formula:

$3x^2 + 60x - 170 = 0 \qquad a = 3, b = 60, c = -170$

$$x = \frac{-b \pm \sqrt{b^2 - 4ac}}{2a}$$

$$x = \frac{-60 \pm \sqrt{60^2 - (4 \times 3 \times -170)}}{2 \times 3}$$

$$x = \frac{-60 \pm \sqrt{5640}}{6}$$

$$x = \frac{-60 + 75.09\ldots}{6} \text{ or } x = \frac{-60 - 75.09\ldots}{6}$$

$x = 2.5167$ or $x = -22.5167$

> Since length cannot be a negative, ignore the negative value of x.

❻ Height of trapezium = 3×2.5167
$= 7.55$cm

> 💡 *Make sure you check that you have answered the question.*

Quick test

❶ Use the quadratic formula to solve the following, giving your answers to 2 decimal places. 🖩
   a) $x^2 + 6x + 2 = 0$ **b)** $2x^2 - 6 = 7x$ **c)** $5x^2 - 5x = 18$

Direct & inverse proportion

Direct proportion U3

The sign $\propto$ means 'is directly proportional to'. This is often abbreviated to 'is proportional to'. For example, $y \propto x^3$ is read as 'y is proportional to x cubed'. $y \propto x$ means that when x is multiplied by a number, then so is the corresponding value of y. For example:

For **direct proportion**, the graph of y against x goes through the origin. For $y \propto x$, the graph is a straight line through the origin.

Inverse proportion U3

$y \propto \frac{1}{x}$ means that y is **inversely proportional** to x: when x is multiplied by a number, then y is divided by that number, and vice versa. For example:

For **inverse proportion**, the graphs of y against x go to infinity when x or $y = 0$.

The graph of $y \propto \frac{1}{x}$ looks like this:

Variation U3

Variation questions are common on GCSE papers and they usually include statements such as:

- 'a is proportional to the square of b'
- 'c is proportional to the square root of d'
- 'p is inversely proportional to a^2'
- 'd varies as the square of x'.

Example

The value (V) of a diamond varies directly with the square of its weight (w). A diamond weighing 5.0g is worth £2500. How heavy is a diamond that is worth £6000?

❶ Change the sentence into a proportionality expression using the symbol $\propto$: $V \propto w^2$

❷ Replace $\propto$ with '$= k$' to make an equation: $V = kw^2$

❸ Substitute the values given in the question in order to find k: $2500 = k \times 5^2$

❹ Rearrange the equation to find the value of k.

$$\frac{2500}{5^2} = k \therefore k = 100$$

❺ Put the value of k back into the equation: $V = 100w^2$

❻ Now answer the question using the equation you have found.

$$6000 = 100 \times w^2$$
$$\frac{6000}{100} = w^2$$
$$w = \sqrt{60}$$
$$w = 7.75g \text{ (2 d.p.)}$$

You use exactly the same steps if y is inversely proportional to x squared, except the equation in ❷ would be $y = \frac{k}{x^2}$

Quick test

❶ y is inversely proportional to the square of x. If $x = 5$ when $y = 4$, work out the value of y when $x = 10$.

❷ p varies as the square root of t. If $t = 16$ when $p = 12$, find the value of p when $t = 49$.

❸ s is inversely proportional to the cube of r. If $r = 2$ when $s = 5$, what is the value of r when $s = 10$?

Linear graphs

Drawing linear (straight-line) graphs · U2

In order to draw a linear (straight-line) graph, follow these easy steps:

1. Choose 3 values of x and draw up a table.
2. Work out the value of y for each value of x.
3. Plot the coordinates and join up the points with a straight line.
4. Label the graph.

Example

Draw the graph of $y = 3x - 1$.

Draw up a table with some suitable values of x. Work out the y values by putting each x value into the equation.

e.g. $x = -2$ ∴ $y = (3 \times -2) - 1$
$= -6 - 1 = -7$

x	-2	0	2
y	-7	-1	5

Plot the points and draw the line.

You need to be able to sketch a linear graph from its equation. If you can do this then you will be able to tell if the graph you have drawn is correct.

Graphs of $y = a$, $x = b$ and $x + y = k$ · U2

$y = a$ is a horizontal line with every y coordinate equal to a.

$x = b$ is a vertical line with every x coordinate equal to b.

Graphs of $x + y = k$, where k is a number, always give linear graphs. Tables of values are not needed when drawing this type of graph.

Example

Draw the graph of $x + y = 3$.

On the x-axis, $y = 0$, so $x = 3$ since $3 + 0 = 3$
On the y-axis, $x = 0$, so $y = 3$ since $0 + 3 = 3$
The graph goes straight through the points (3, 0) and (0, 3).

Interpreting $y = mx + c$ | U2

The general equation of a linear graph is
$$y = mx + c$$
where m is the gradient (steepness) of the line.

Remember these points about linear graphs:
- As m increases the line gets steeper.
- If m is positive, the line slopes forwards.
- If m is negative, the line slopes backwards.
- c is the intercept on the y-axis, that is, where the graph cuts the y-axis.
- Parallel lines have the same gradient.

Example

Write down the equation of a line that is parallel to $y = 5 - 3x$ and that goes through the point (0, 2).

❶ Rewrite the equation in the form $y = mx + c$,
so $y = -3x + 5$

❷ Since parallel lines have the same gradient:
$y = -3x + c$
Line goes through (0, 2), hence $c = 2$

❸ Equation of straight line is $y = -3x + 2$ or $y = 2 - 3x$

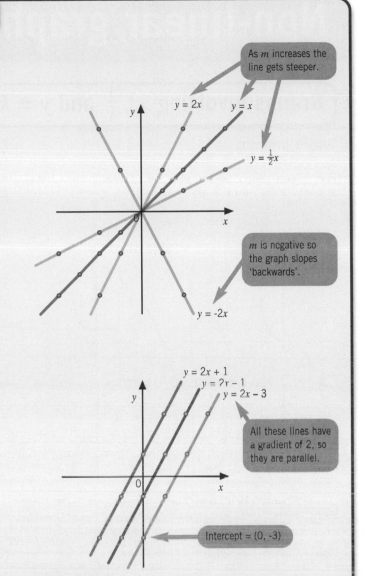

As m increases the line gets steeper.

m is negative so the graph slopes 'backwards'.

All these lines have a gradient of 2, so they are parallel.

Intercept = (0, -3)

Algebra

Finding the gradient of a line | U2

To find the **gradient** (steepness) of a line, follow these steps:
❶ Choose two points on the line.
❷ Draw a triangle as shown.
❸ Find the change in y (height) and the change in x (base).
❹ Gradient = $\dfrac{\text{change in } y}{\text{change in } x}$ or $\dfrac{\text{height}}{\text{base}}$ = $\dfrac{4}{3} = 1\tfrac{1}{3}$
❺ Decide if the gradient is positive or negative.

Quick test

❶ Draw the graph of $y = 6 - 2x$. From your graph, write down the solution of the following equations.
   a) $6 - 2x = 4$ b) $6 - 2x = 3$

❷ Write down the gradient and y-axis intercept for each of these linear graphs.
   a) $y = 4 + 2x$ b) $y = 3x - 2$ c) $2y = 6x + 4$

Non-linear graphs

Graphs involving x^3, $\frac{1}{x}$ and $y = k^x$

Graphs involving x^3

An equation of the form

$$y = ax^3 + bx^2 + cx + d$$

is called a **cubic** where $a \neq 0$.

For $a > 0$, the graph of a cubic takes one of these forms:

For $a < 0$, the overall trend is reversed:

Graphs involving $\frac{1}{x}$

An equation of the form $y = \frac{a}{x}$ takes two basic forms depending on the value of a.

$a > 0$ $a < 0$

Graphs approach but do not touch the axes.

Graphs involving $y = k^x$

Graphs involving $y = k^x$, where k is a positive number, are called exponential expressions.

A sketch of the graph $y = 2^x$ looks like this:

$y = 2^x$

The graph $y = 2^x$ has no maximum or minimum point. It crosses the y-axis at the point (0, 1). The value of y increases rapidly as the value of x increases. When x is negative, the value of y approaches zero. The graph never crosses the x-axis.

Example

Draw the graph of $y = x^2 + 4 + \frac{2}{x}$ for $-3 \leqslant x \leqslant 3$.

❶ Make a table of values:

x	x^2	4	$+\frac{2}{x}$	y
-3	9	4	-0.6̇	12.3̇
-2	4	4	-1	7
-1	1	4	-2	3
-0.5	0.25	4	-4	0.25
-0.2	0.04	4	-10	-5.96
0.2	0.04	4	10	14.04
0.5	0.25	4	4	8.25
1	1	4	2	7
2	4	4	1	9
3	9	4	0.6̇	13.6̇

There is no zero row since you cannot calculate $\frac{2}{x}$ if $x = 0$.

❷ Plot the points and draw a smooth curve (see graph $y = x^2 + 4 + \frac{2}{x}$ below).

There will be a break in the curve at $x = 0$.

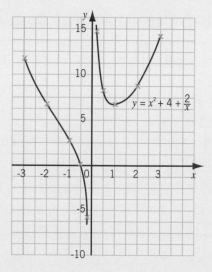

$y = x^2 + 4 + \frac{2}{x}$

Graphs of the form $y = ax^2 + bx + c$ are called **quadratic graphs** where $a \neq 0$. These graphs are curved and known as **parabolas**.

If $a > 0$, then the graph is U-shaped.

If $a < 0$, then the graph has an upside-down U.

Example

Draw the graph of $y = x^2 - x - 6$ using values of x from -2 to 3. Use the graph to find the value of x when $y = -3$.

When drawing a quadratic graph follow these steps:

❶ Make a table of values. Work out the values of y by substituting the values of x into the equation:

e.g. If $x = 1$, $y = x^2 - x - 6 = 1^2 - 1 - 6 = -6$

x	-2	-1	0	1	2	3	0.5
y	0	-4	-6	-6	-4	0	-6.25

$x = 0.5$ is worked out to find the minimum value.

❷ Plot the points and join them with a smooth curve.

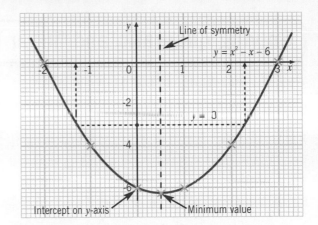

💡 *Draw the curve with a sharp pencil. Go through all the points and check for any parts that look wrong.*

The graph shows the following:

- The **minimum value** is when $x = 0.5$, $y = -6.25$.
- The **line of symmetry** is at $x = 0.5$.
- The curve cuts the y-axis at $(0, -6)$, i.e. $(0, c)$.
- When $y = -3$, read across from $y = -3$ to the graph then read up to the x-axis: $x = 2.3$ and $x = 1.3$.

  These are the approximate solutions of the equation $x^2 - x - 6 = -3$.

Algebra

Quick test

❶ a) Complete the table of values for the graph $y = x^3 + 3$. 🖩

x	-3	-2	-1	0	1	2	3
y							

b) Draw the graph of $y = x^3 + 3$. Use scales of 1 unit per 2cm on the x-axis and 10 units per 2cm on the y-axis.

c) From your graph, find the value of x when $y = 15$.

❷ Match each of the four graphs below with one of the following equations.
- $y = 2x - 5$
- $y = x^2 + 3$
- $y = 3 - x^2$
- $y = 5 - x$
- $y = x^3$
- $y = \dfrac{2}{x}$

Graph A   Graph B   Graph C   Graph D

Advanced graphs

Solving quadratic and linear equations simultaneously U2 U3

We have already seen that the point where two graphs meet represents the simultaneous solutions of the equations. So far we have only looked at linear equations and their corresponding straight-line graphs. You also need to be able to work out the coordinates of the points of intersection of a straight line and a quadratic curve.

The diagram shows the points of intersection of the straight line $y = 5x - 6$ and the curve $y = x^2$.

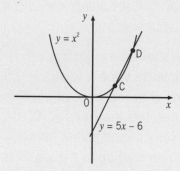

To find the coordinates of the points of intersection, C and D, of the line $y = 5x - 6$ and the curve $y = x^2$, we know that the points C and D both lie on the curve and the line, giving us the simultaneous equations:

$y = 5x - 6$ ① $y = x^2$ ②

❶ Eliminate y by substituting equation ② into equation ① (or by subtracting equation ① from equation ②): $x^2 = 5x - 6$

❷ Rearrange: $x^2 - 5x + 6 = 0$

❸ Factorise; $(x - 2)(x - 3) = 0$
and solve: $x = 2$ and $x = 3$
These are the x coordinates of the points of intersection.

❹ Substitute the values of x back in equation ① to find the y coordinates:

$x = 2$: $y = 5x - 6$
            $y = 5 \times 2 - 6$
            $y = 4$ Coordinate of C (2, 4)

$x = 3$: $y = 5x - 6$
            $y = 5 \times 3 - 6$
            $y = 9$ Coordinate of D (3, 9)

So the line $y = 5x - 6$ intersects the curve $y = x^2$ at (2, 4) and (3, 9).

Remember, solving a quadratic and a linear equation gives the point of intersection of the two graphs.

The intersection of a quadratic and a line U2 U3

Example

Find the coordinates of the points of intersection of the line $y = 3x + 4$ and the graph $y = x^2 + x - 4$ using an algebraic method.

We know that the points of intersection lie on the curve and the line, giving us the simultaneous equations:

$y = 3x + 4$ ①
$y = x^2 + x - 4$ ②

❶ Eliminate y by substituting equation ① into equation ②
$3x + 4 = x^2 + x - 4$

❷ Rearrange: $0 = x^2 + x - 4 - 3x - 4$
    $x^2 - 2x - 8 = 0$

❸ Factorise: $(x - 4)(x + 2) = 0$
And solve: $x = 4$ or $x = -2$
These are the x coordinates of the points of intersection.

❹ Substitute the x values back into equation ①
$y = 3x + 4$
$x = 4, y = 16$
$x = -2, y = -2$
The line $y = 3x + 4$ intersects the curve $y = x^2 + x - 4$ at the points (-2, -2) and (4, 16).

Algebra

Functions and transformations

If $y = $ 'an expression involving x' then it can be written as $y = f(x)$.

The graphs of related functions can be found by applying the following **transformations**:

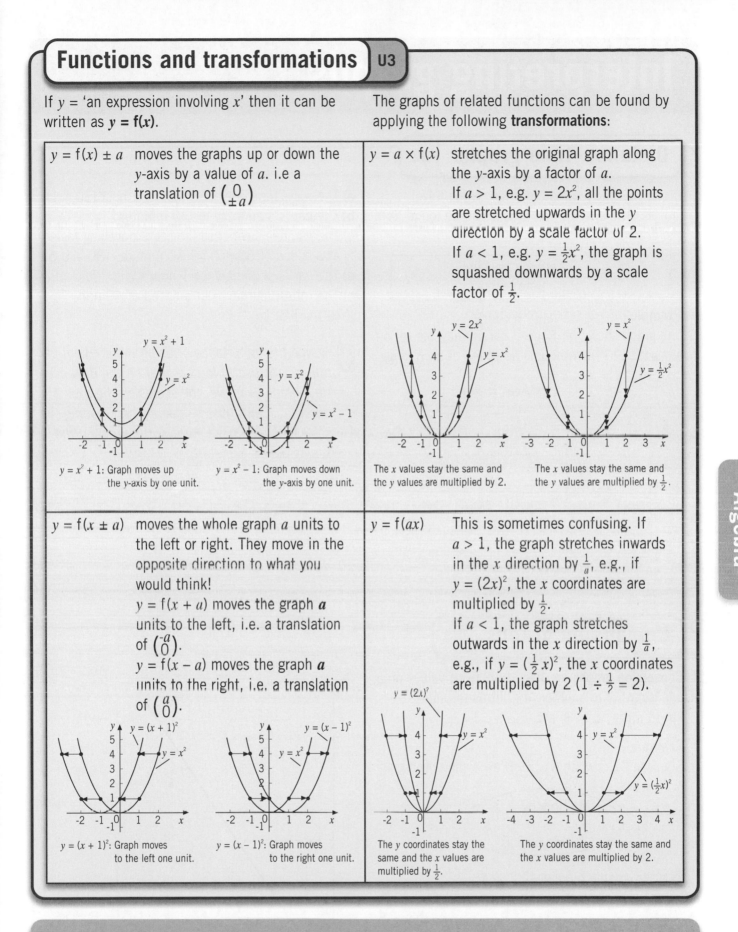

$y = f(x) \pm a$ moves the graphs up or down the y-axis by a value of a. i.e a translation of $\begin{pmatrix} 0 \\ \pm a \end{pmatrix}$

$y = x^2 + 1$: Graph moves up the y-axis by one unit.

$y = x^2 - 1$: Graph moves down the y-axis by one unit.

$y = a \times f(x)$ stretches the original graph along the y-axis by a factor of a.
If $a > 1$, e.g. $y = 2x^2$, all the points are stretched upwards in the y direction by a scale factor of 2.
If $a < 1$, e.g. $y = \frac{1}{2}x^2$, the graph is squashed downwards by a scale factor of $\frac{1}{2}$.

The x values stay the same and the y values are multiplied by 2.

The x values stay the same and the y values are multiplied by $\frac{1}{2}$.

$y = f(x \pm a)$ moves the whole graph a units to the left or right. They move in the opposite direction to what you would think!
$y = f(x + a)$ moves the graph a units to the left, i.e. a translation of $\begin{pmatrix} -a \\ 0 \end{pmatrix}$.
$y = f(x - a)$ moves the graph a units to the right, i.e. a translation of $\begin{pmatrix} a \\ 0 \end{pmatrix}$.

$y = (x + 1)^2$: Graph moves to the left one unit.

$y = (x - 1)^2$: Graph moves to the right one unit.

$y = f(ax)$ This is sometimes confusing. If $a > 1$, the graph stretches inwards in the x direction by $\frac{1}{a}$, e.g., if $y = (2x)^2$, the x coordinates are multiplied by $\frac{1}{2}$.
If $a < 1$, the graph stretches outwards in the x direction by $\frac{1}{a}$, e.g., if $y = (\frac{1}{2}x)^2$, the x coordinates are multiplied by 2 $(1 \div \frac{1}{2} = 2)$.

The y coordinates stay the same and the x values are multiplied by $\frac{1}{2}$.

The y coordinates stay the same and the x values are multiplied by 2.

Algebra

Quick test

1 Sketch the following graphs.
   a) $y = x^3$ **b)** $y = x^3 - 4$
   c) $y = (x - 2)^3$ **d)** $y = 2x^3$

2 Solve the simultaneous equations $y = x^2$ and $y = 3x + 4$.

Interpreting graphs

Distance–time graphs · U2

Distance–time graphs are often called **travel graphs**. The **speed** of an object can be found from the gradient of the line.

$$\text{Speed} = \frac{\text{distance travelled}}{\text{time taken}}$$

Example
The graph shows Mr Rogers' car journey. He set off at 9am (0900). Work out the speed of each stage.

a) The car is travelling at 30mph for 1 hour (30 ÷ 1).
b) The car is stationary for 30 minutes.
c) The graph is steeper so the car is travelling faster, at a speed of 60mph for 30 minutes (30 ÷ 0.5).
d) The car is stationary for 1 hour.
e) The return journey is at a speed of 40mph (60 ÷ 1.5)

> *Notice the importance of using the gradient of a line. It is useful to note that on the distance–time graph example, the scales on the axes are different. Care must be taken when reading the scales: always make sure you understand the scales before you start.*

Conversion graphs · U3

Conversion graphs are used to convert values of one quantity to another, e.g. litres to pints, km to miles, £ to $, etc.

Example
Suppose £1 is worth $1.50. Draw a conversion graph.

£1 — Multiply by 1.5 → $1.50
$1.50 — Divide by 1.5 → £1

① Make a table of values.

£	1	2	3	4	5
$	1.5	3.0	4.5	6.0	7.5

× 1.5

② Plot each of these points on the graph paper.
③ To change $ to £, read across to the line then down, e.g. $4 is £2.65 (approx.).
④ To change £ to $, read up to the line then across, e.g. £4.50 is $6.80 (approx.).

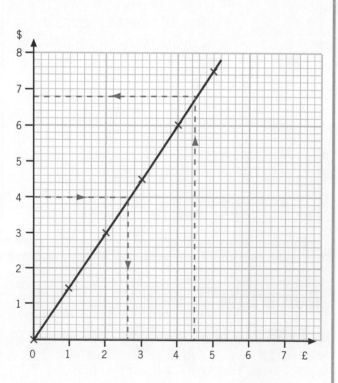

Algebra

Using graphs to solve equations | U3

A graph can be used to solve equations. Often, the equation needs to be rearranged in order to resemble the equation of the plotted graph.

Example

The graph $y = x^2 - 2x + 1$ is drawn opposite.
Use the graph to solve the following equations:

a) $x^2 - 2x + 1 = 6$

Our graph is $y = x^2 - 2x + 1$. The solutions are where the line $y = 6$ crosses the graph:
$x = -1.45$, and $x = 3.45$

b) $x^2 - 3x = 0$

We need to rearrange the equation so it is like our graph:

$x^2 - 3x = 0$
$x^2 - 3x + x + 1 = x + 1$ Add $x + 1$ to both sides.
$x^2 - 2x + 1 = x + 1$

Our graph is $y = x^2 - 2x + 1$. The solutions are where the graph crosses the line $y = x + 1$:
$x = 0$ and $x = 3$.

Using graphs to find relationships | U3

Sometimes you will be given a table of data that is known to fit a relationship. If a suitable graph is drawn, the relationship can be found.

Example

The graph below is known to fit the relationship $y = pq^x$ where p and q are positive constants.
Use the graph to find the values of p and q and the relationship.

In order to find values for p and q, we need to take values at R and S, then substitute them into the equation $y = pq^x$.

At point R, $x = 0$ and $y = 4$
So $y = pq^x$ becomes

$4 = p \times q^0$ Remember, $q^0 = 1$.
$4 = p$

At point S, $x = 2$ and $y = 16$
So
$16 = 4 \times q^2$
$16 \div 4 = q^2$ Divide both sides by 4.
$4 = q^2$
$q = \sqrt{4} = 2$

The relationship is $y = 4 \times 2^x$.

Quick test

1 These containers are being filled with a liquid at a rate of 150ml per second. The graphs show how the depth of the water (d) changes with time (t). Match the containers with the graphs opposite.

2 Draw the graph of $y = x^2 + x - 2$.
Use your graph to solve the following equations.
  a) $x^2 + x = 5$ **b)** $x^2 - 2 = 0$ **c)** $x^2 - 2x - 2 = 0$

Practice questions

Use these questions to test your progress. Check your answers on pages 111–112. You may wish to answer these questions on a separate piece of paper so that you can show full working out, which you will be expected to do in the exam.

① Here are the first five terms of a number sequence: 7, 11, 15, 19, 23.
Write down an expression for the nth term of the sequence.

U2

② Simplify:

a) $3x^2 \times 4x^2$

b) $6x^2y \times 2x^3y^2$

c) $12y^4 \div 3y$

d) $(3y^2)^2$

③ Solve the simultaneous equations:
$4a + 3b = 6$
$2a - 3b = 12$

④ Factorise and then solve this quadratic equation: $2x^2 - 13x + 18 = 0$

⑤ Solve the inequality $2 \leqslant 5n - 3 \leqslant 12$

⑥ Solve these equations by completing the square. Leave your answer in surd form.

a) $x^2 - 4x + 1 = 0$

b) $x^2 - 8x + 10 = 0$

⑦ If the area of the rectangle is 50cm²:
a) show that $x^2 + x - 27 = 0$

(2x + 4)cm

(x − 1)cm   Area = 50cm²

b) work out the length of the rectangle.

⑧ Make p the subject of the formula $6p + 2r = x(4 - p)$.

⑨ Ria says, 'the sum of the squares of two odd numbers is always even'.
Prove this algebraically.

⑩ Simplify $\sqrt{\dfrac{\pi a^3}{16\pi a}}$

11 Solve the following equations. **U2 U3**
   a) $2x + 4 = 10$ **b)** $3x - 1 = 11$ **c)** $5x - 3 = 2x + 12$
   d) $3(x + 1) = 9$ **e)** $2(x + 1) = x + 3$

12 Simplify: **a)** $\dfrac{2}{(x + 4)} + \dfrac{3}{(x - 2)}$ **b)** $\dfrac{6}{x - 3} - \dfrac{2}{x + 4}$ **c)** $\dfrac{4a^2b}{a^4b} \times \dfrac{a^3b^2}{8ab^2}$

13 $P^2 = 5xy - 3x^2$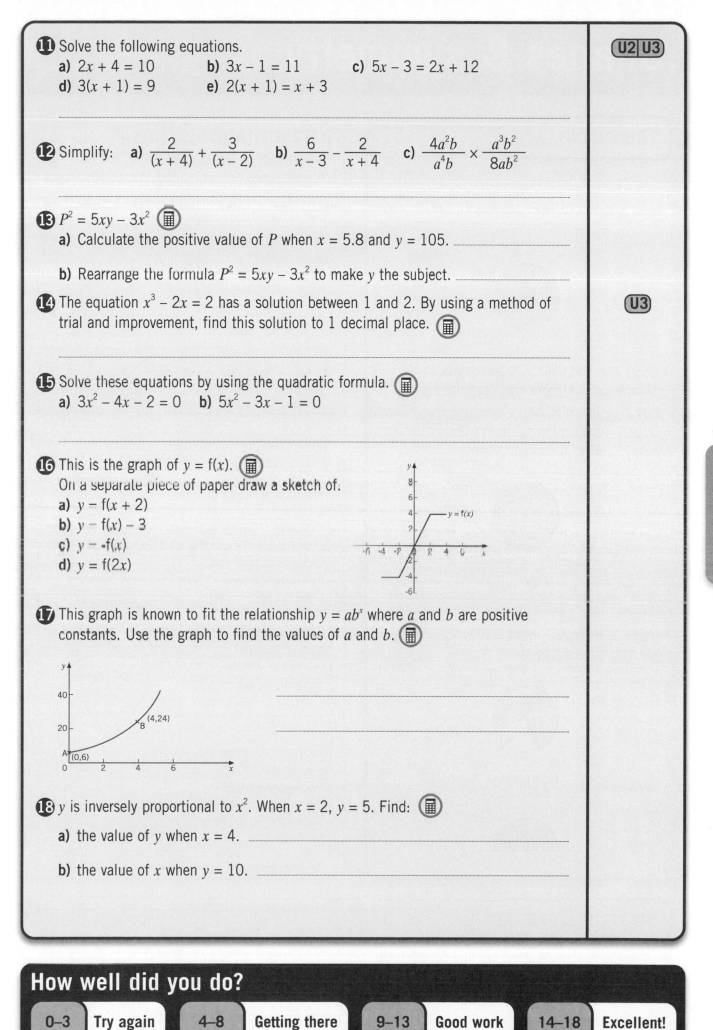
   a) Calculate the positive value of P when $x = 5.8$ and $y = 105$. _____

   b) Rearrange the formula $P^2 = 5xy - 3x^2$ to make y the subject. _____

14 The equation $x^3 - 2x = 2$ has a solution between 1 and 2. By using a method of **U3**
   trial and improvement, find this solution to 1 decimal place.

15 Solve these equations by using the quadratic formula.
   a) $3x^2 - 4x - 2 = 0$ **b)** $5x^2 - 3x - 1 = 0$

16 This is the graph of $y = f(x)$.
   On a separate piece of paper draw a sketch of.
   a) $y = f(x + 2)$
   b) $y = f(x) - 3$
   c) $y = -f(x)$
   d) $y = f(2x)$

17 This graph is known to fit the relationship $y = ab^x$ where a and b are positive
   constants. Use the graph to find the values of a and b.

18 y is inversely proportional to x^2. When $x = 2$, $y = 5$. Find:

   a) the value of y when $x = 4$. _____

   b) the value of x when $y = 10$. _____

How well did you do?

| 0–3 | Try again | 4–8 | Getting there | 9–13 | Good work | 14–18 | Excellent! |

Shapes & symmetry

Geometry and measures

The circle `U3`

Diameter = 2 × radius.
The **circumference** is the distance around the outside edge.

A **chord** is a line that joins two points on the circumference. A chord that goes through the centre is a diameter.
A **tangent** touches the circle at one point only.
An **arc** is part of the circumference.

A **sector** is a part of a circle enclosed between two radii.
A **segment** is formed when chords divide the circle into different parts.

A **semicircle** is half a circle.

Quadrilaterals `U3`

Quadrilaterals are four-sided shapes. You need to be able to sketch these shapes and know their symmetrical properties.

Square	
Four lines of symmetry Rotational symmetry of order 4	
Rectangle	
Two lines of symmetry Rotational symmetry of order 2	
Parallelogram	
No lines of symmetry Rotational symmetry of order 2	
Rhombus	
Two lines of symmetry Rotational symmetry of order 2 Diagonals bisect at 90°	
Kite	
One line of symmetry No rotational symmetry	
Trapezium	
Isosceles trapezium: One line of symmetry Trapezium: No rotational symmetry	Isosceles trapezium Trapezium

Straight lines `U3`

Infinitely long straight lines are just called **lines**.

——————————————— ← Line

Lines that have a definite start and finish are called **line segments**.

A ——————————— B Line Segment

Parallel lines are the lines that remain the same distance apart, i.e. they never meet.

Reflective symmetry U3

Reflective symmetry is when both sides of a symmetrical shape are the same when the mirror line is drawn across it. The mirror line is known as the **line** or **axis of symmetry**.

The diagram shows how the line of symmetry can act as a mirror line. The reflected shape is exactly the same as the object.

1 line of symmetry

1 line of symmetry

3 lines of symmetry

No lines of symmetry

You may be asked to complete an object with a specific number of lines of symmetry. Draw the reflected shape carefully using a ruler.

Rotational symmetry U3

A 2D (two-dimensional) shape has rotational symmetry if, when turned about the centre, it looks exactly the same.

The **order of rotational symmetry** is the number of times the shape looks the same within one complete turn (360°). For the letter M, the shape has 1 such position. It is said to have **rotational symmetry of order 1**, or **no** rotational symmetry. The same is true for letter T.

Order 1

Order 1

Order 3

Order 4

Quick test

1. The dashed lines are the lines of symmetry. Complete the shape so that it is symmetrical.

2. Fill in the missing labels.

   a) _____

   b) _____

   c) _____

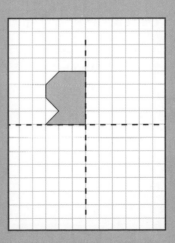

Measures & measurement

Metric and imperial units — U3

Length	Weight	Capacity
10mm = 1cm	1000mg = 1g	1000ml = 1 litre
100cm = 1m	1000g = 1kg	100cl = 1 litre
1000m = 1km	1000kg = 1 tonne	$1000cm^3$ = 1 litre

Length	Weight	Capacity
1 foot = 12 inches	1 stone = 14 pounds (lb)	20 fluid oz = 1 pint
1 yard = 3 feet	1 pound = 16 ounces (oz)	8 pints = 1 gallon

Compound measures — U3

Speed can be measured in kilometres per hour (km/h), miles per hour (mph) and metres per second (m/s). km/h, mph and m/s are all **compound measures** because they involve a combination of basic measures.

Speed

$$\text{Average speed} = \frac{\text{total distance travelled}}{\text{total time taken}}$$
$$s = \frac{d}{t}$$

Always check the units before starting a question. Change them if necessary.

Example

A car travels 50 miles in 1 hour 20 minutes. Find the speed in miles per hour.

Change the time units first:

20 minutes = $\frac{20}{60}$ = $\frac{1}{3}$ of 1 hour = $0.\dot{3}$ of 1 hour

$$s = \frac{d}{t} = \frac{50}{1.\dot{3}} = 37.5\text{mph}$$

From the speed formula, two other formulae can be found.

$$\text{Time} = \frac{\text{distance}}{\text{speed}} \quad \text{Distance} = \text{speed} \times \text{time}$$
$$s = \frac{d}{t} \qquad t = \frac{d}{s} \qquad d = st$$

💡 *Just remember the letters:*

Example

A car travels a distance of 238 miles at an average speed of 68mph.

How long does it take?

$\text{Time} = \frac{\text{distance}}{\text{speed}}$, so $t = \frac{238}{68} = 3.5$ hours

3.5 hours must be changed into hours and minutes to do this:

1. Subtract the hours: 3.5 − 3 = 0.5
2. Multiply the decimal part by 60 minutes.
   0.5 × 60 = 30 minutes (nearest minute)
3. Time taken = 3 hours 30 minutes

Density

$$\text{Density} = \frac{\text{mass}}{\text{volume}} \qquad \text{Volume} = \frac{\text{mass}}{\text{density}}$$
$$\text{Mass} = \text{density} \times \text{volume}$$
$$D = \frac{M}{V} \qquad V = \frac{M}{D} \qquad M = DV$$

Example

Find the density of an object whose mass is 400g and whose volume is 25cm^3.

Density = $\frac{M}{V} = \frac{400}{25} = 16\text{g/cm}^3$

Since the mass is in grams and volume is in cm^3, density is in g/cm^3.

Geometry and measures

Comparisons between metric and imperial units U3

Length	Weight	Capacity
2.5cm ≈ 1 inch	25g ≈ 1 ounce	1 litre ≈ $1\frac{3}{4}$ pints
30cm ≈ 1 foot	1kg ≈ 2.2 pounds	4.5 litres ≈ 1 gallon
1m ≈ 39 inches		
8km ≈ 5 miles		

There is a lot of learning to do in this section. Try to learn all the metric and imperial conversions, and the formulae for speed and density.

Most conversions between metric and imperial units are only approximate.

Example
Change 25km into miles.

$$8km ≈ 5 \text{ miles}$$
$$1km ≈ \frac{5}{8} \text{ mile} = 0.625 \text{ miles}$$
$$25km ≈ 25 × 0.625$$
$$= 15.625 \text{ miles} ≈ 16 \text{ miles}$$

Accuracy of measurement U1 U3

There are two types of measurements: discrete measurements and continuous measurements.
- **Discrete measures** are quantities that can be counted; for example, the number of baked bean tins on a shelf.
- **Continuous measures** are measurements which have been made by using a measuring instrument; for example, the height of a person. Continuous measures are not exact.

Example
Nigel weighs 72kg to the nearest kg. His actual weight could be anywhere between 71.5kg and 72.5kg.

If W represents weight, then:
$$71.5 ≤ W < 72.5$$

This is the **lower limit** of Nigel's weight (sometimes known as the **lower bound**). Anything below 71.5kg would be recorded as 71kg.

This is the **upper limit** (**upper bound**) of Nigel's weight. Anything from 72.5kg upwards would be recorded as 73kg. Anything below would be recorded as 72kg.

Quick test

1. Change 3500g into kg.
2. Change 3kg into pounds.
3. Change 6 litres into pints.
4. Write down the upper and lower limits for a time of 9.2 seconds, rounded to the nearest tenth of a second.
5. Write down the upper and lower limits for a weight of 58kg, rounded to the nearest kg.
6. Amy walks 6 miles in 2 hours 40 minutes. Find her average speed. 🖩
7. Find the time taken for a car to travel 600 miles at an average speed of 70mph 🖩
8. Find the density of an object whose mass is 20g and whose volume is 9cm^3. 🖩

Transformations 1

Transformations · U3

A transformation changes the position or size of a shape. Transformations are often used in the creation of repeating wallpaper patterns.

There are four types of transformations: translations, reflections, rotations and enlargements.

Translations · U3

A translation moves a figure from one place to another. The size and shape of the figure are not changed. **Vectors** are used to describe the distance and direction of a translation.

A vector is written $\binom{a}{b}$. a represents the **horizontal** movement, and b represents the **vertical** movement.

ABC, P and Q are **congruent** – two shapes are congruent if they have exactly the same size and shape.

Example
a) Translate ABC by the vector $\binom{2}{1}$. Call it P.

> This means 2 to the right and 1 upwards.

b) Translate ABC by the vector $\binom{-3}{-2}$. Call it Q.

> This means 3 to the left and 2 down.

Reflections · U3

A reflection creates an image of an object on the other side of the mirror line. The mirror line is known as an **axis of reflection**. The size and shape of the figure are not changed.

Example
Reflect triangle ABC in:
a) the x axis, and call it D
b) the line $y = -x$, and call it E
c) the line $x = 5$, and call it F.

D, E and F are congruent to triangle ABC.

When describing reflections make sure you write down the equation of the mirror line.

> Count the squares from the object to the mirror line. The image will be the same distance away.

Rotations U3

A rotation turns a figure through an angle about some fixed point. This fixed point is called the **centre of rotation**. The size and shape of the figure are not changed.

Example
Rotate triangle ABC:
a) 90° clockwise about (0, 0) and call it R
b) 180° about (0, 0), and call it S
c) 90° anticlockwise about (-1, 1), and call it T.

Triangles R, S and T are all congruent to triangle ABC.

When describing a rotation give:
- the centre of rotation
- the direction of the turn (clockwise or anticlockwise)
- the angle of the turn.

If you don't give all three pieces of information, you will lose marks for not describing the rotation fully.

Quick test

1. On the diagram alongside:
   a) Translate triangle ABC by the vector $\binom{-3}{1}$. Call it P.
   b) Reflect ABC in the line $y = x$. Call it Q.
   c) Reflect ABC in the line $y = -1$. Call it R.
   d) Rotate ABC 180° about (0, 0). Call it S.

2. What does the vector $\binom{-2}{3}$ mean?

3. A point X (3, -6) moves to the point Y (-2, 5). What is the vector translation that moves point X to point Y?

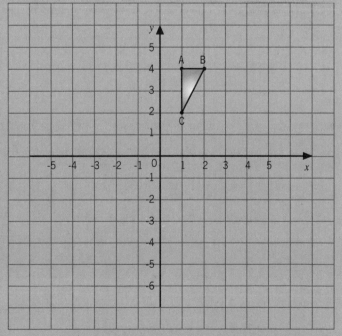

Transformations 2

Enlargements U3

An enlargement changes the size but not the shape of an object. The **centre of enlargement** is the point from which the enlargement takes place. The **scale factor** indicates how many times the lengths of the original figure have increased in size. Remember the following:

- If the scale factor is greater than 1, the shape becomes bigger.
- If the scale factor is less than 1, the shape becomes smaller.
- When one shape is an enlargement of another, they are **similar**, i.e. they are the same shape with the same angles, but different sizes.

Examples

a) Enlarge triangle ABC by a scale factor of 2, centre = (0, 0). Call it A'B'C'.
Notice each side of the enlargement is twice the length of the original.
e.g. A'B' = 2AB

b) Describe fully the transformation that maps ABCDEF onto A'B'C'D'E'F'.

- To find the centre of enlargement, join A to A', and continue the line. Join B to B', and continue the line. Do the same for the others.

- Where all the lines meet is the centre of enlargement: (-1, 3).
- The transformation is an enlargement with scale factor $\frac{1}{3}$ and centre of enlargement at (-1, 3).

Enlargement with a negative scale factor U3

If the scale factor of an enlargement is negative, then the image is drawn on the opposite side of the centre of enlargement to the object. The image will also be rotated by half a turn.

Example

The triangle ABC has been mapped onto $A_1B_1C_1$ by a scale factor of -2, centre at O.

> *When asked to describe an enlargement, you must include both the scale factor and the position of the centre of enlargement.*

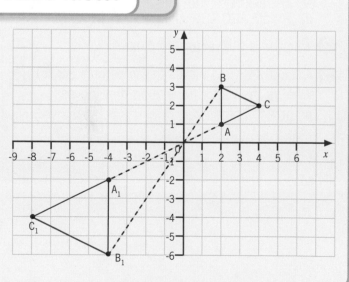

Combining transformations | U3

Transformations can be combined in a series of two or more transformations.

Example

a) Reflect ABC in the x-axis.
   Call the image $A_1B_1C_1$.

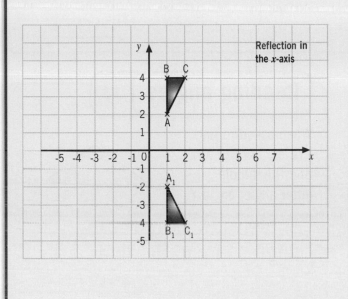

Reflection in the x-axis

b) Reflect $A_1B_1C_1$ in the y-axis.
   Call the image $A_2B_2C_2$.

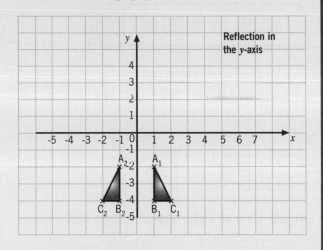

Reflection in the y-axis

The single transformation that maps ABC directly onto $A_2B_2C_2$ is a rotation of 180° about centre (0, 0).

Rotation of 180° centre (0,0)

Quick test

1. Draw an enlargement of shape P with a scale factor of 2, centre of enlargement as shown. Call it P_1.

2. a) Rotate the shaded shape through a 90° clockwise rotation about (0, 0). Call this shape B.

   b) Reflect shape B in the x-axis and call this shape C.

1

2

Angles

Types of angles | U3

An **acute angle** is between 0° and 90°.

An **obtuse angle** is between 90° and 180°.

A **reflex angle** is between 180° and 360°.

A **right angle** is 90°.

Angle facts | U3

Angles on a straight line add up to **180°**.
$a + b + c = 180°$

Angles at a point add up to **360°**.
$a + b + c + d = 360°$

Angles in a triangle add up to **180°**.
$a + b + c = 180°$

Angles in a quadrilateral add up to **360°**.
$a + b + c + d = 360°$

Vertically-opposite angles are **equal**.
$a = b, c = d$
$a + d = b + c = 180°$

An **exterior angle** of a triangle equals the sum of the **two opposite interior angles**.
$a + b = c$

Reading angles | U3

When asked to find XYZ or ∠XYZ or XŶZ, find the **middle letter** angle, angle Y.

Angles in parallel lines | U3

Alternate (z) angles are **equal**.	
Corresponding angles are **equal**.	
Supplementary (allied) angles add up to **180°**: $c + d = 180°$	

Examples
Find the angles labelled by letters.

a) $a = 180° - 50° - 70° = 60°$
$b = 180° - 60° = 120°$
or $b = 50° + 70° = 120°$

b) $a + 80° + 40° + 85° = 360°$
$a = 360° - 205°$
$a = 155°$

c) $a = 120°$ (angles on a straight line)
$b = 60°$ (vertically opposite to 60°)
$c = 60°$ (corresponding to b or alternate to 60°)
$d = 60°$ (vertically opposite to c)

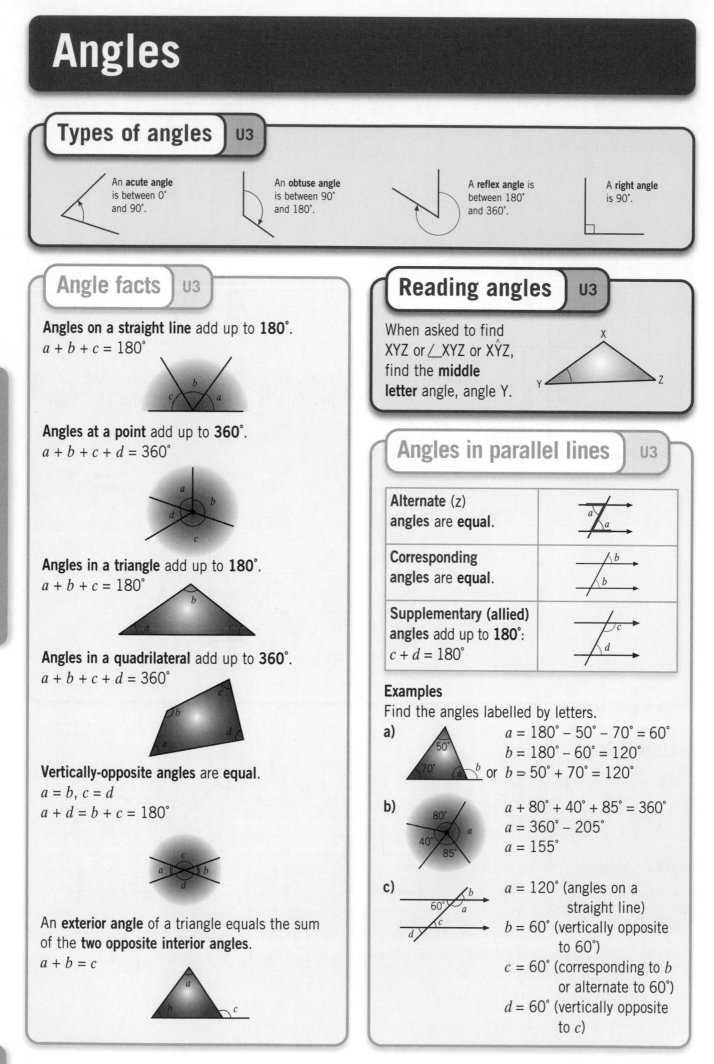

Polygons U3

Polygons are 2D shapes with straight sides. **Regular polygons** are shapes with all sides and angles equal.

Number of sides	Name of polygon
3	Triangle
4	Quadrilateral
5	Pentagon
6	Hexagon
7	Heptagon
8	Octagon
9	Nonagon
10	Decagon

Tessellations U3

A tessellation is a pattern of 2D shapes that fit together without leaving any gaps.

For shapes to tessellate, the angles at each point must add up to 360°.

For example, regular pentagons will not tessellate. Each interior angle is 108°, and 3 × 108° = 324°. A gap of 360° − 324° = 36° is left.

M.C. Escher is a famous artist who used tessellations in his art work. Tessellations are often seen in mosaics and floor tiles.

Angles in a polygon U3

There are two types of angle in any polygon: **interior** (inside) and **exterior** (outside).

For a regular polygon with n sides:
- sum of exterior angles = 360°, so each exterior angle $= \dfrac{360°}{n}$
- interior angle + exterior angle = 180°
- sum of interior angles = $(n - 2) \times 180°$ or $(2n - 4) \times 90°$

Examples

a) A regular polygon has an interior angle of 150°. How many sides does it have?

❶ Let n be the number of sides.
Exterior + interior = 180°
Exterior angle = 180° − 150° = 30°
Exterior angle $= \dfrac{360°}{n}$

❷ So $n = \dfrac{360°}{\text{exterior angle}} = \dfrac{360°}{30°} = 12$

The polygon has 12 sides (it is a dodecahedron).

b) The diagram shows an irregular pentagon. Work out the size of x.

Sum of interior angles:
$(5 - 2) \times 180°$
$= 3 \times 180°$
$= 540°$

Form an equation and solve it to find x:
$x + 2x + x + 30° + 3x + 3x + 10° = 540°$
$10x + 40° = 540°$
$10x = 540° - 40°$
$10x = 500°$
$x = 50°$

❗ If you are asked to 'Explain' in an angle question, always refer to the angle properties, e.g. angles on a straight line add up to 180°.

Quick test

❶ Find the sizes of the angles labelled by letters.

a)

b)

c)

❷ Find the size of an a) exterior and b) interior angle of a regular pentagon.
❸ Explain whether a regular hexagon will tessellate.

Bearings & scale drawings

Bearings U3

A **bearing** is the direction travelled between two points, given as an angle in degrees:
- All bearings are measured **clockwise from the north** line.
- All bearings should be given as three figures, e.g. 225°, 043°, 006°.

Back bearings

How to find the **back bearing** (the bearing of Q from P in the examples below):
1 Draw in a north line at P.
2 The two north lines are parallel lines, so the angle properties of parallel lines can be used.

💡 *The word 'from' is important when answering bearing questions. It tells you where to put the north line and where to measure.*

Bearings (measure from the north line at Q)	Back bearings (measure from the north line at P)
a) i) Bearing of P from Q = 060°	**a) ii)** Bearing of Q from P = 60° + 180° = 240°
b) i) Bearing of P from Q = 180° − 30° = 150°	**b) ii)** Bearing of Q from P = 360° − 30° = 330°
c) i) Bearing of P from Q = 360° − 50° = 310°	**c) ii)** Bearing of Q from P = 180° − 50° = 130°

Scale drawings and bearings U3

Scale drawings are useful for finding lengths and angles. They are often used by architects and surveyors.

Example

A ship sails from a harbour for 15km on a bearing of 040°, then continues due east for 20km. Make a scale drawing of this journey using a scale of 1cm to 5km. How far will the ship have to sail to get back to the harbour by the shortest route? What will the bearing be?

Shortest route = 6.4 × 5km = 32km
Bearing back to harbour = 70° + 180° = 250°

Note – this diagram is not drawn accurately but is used to show you what your diagram should look like.

Scales and maps

Scales are often used on maps. They are usually written as a ratio. You will use map work in geography. Orienteers use maps and compasses to find directions.

Example

The scale on a road map is 1 : 25000. Bury and Oldham are 60cm apart on the map. Work out the real distance, in km, between Bury and Oldham.

❶ Scale 1 : 25000, distance on map is 60cm.
∴ Real distance = 60 × 25000 = 1500000cm

❷ Divide by 100 to change cm to m:
1500000 ÷ 100 = 15000m

❸ Divide by 1000 to change m to km:
15000 ÷ 1000 = 15km

> A scale of 1 : 25000 means that 1cm on the scale drawing represents a real length of 25000cm (0.25km).

Quick test

❶ What are the bearings of A from B in the following?

❷ For each of the questions above, work out the bearing of B from A.

❸ The scale on a road map is 1 : 50000. If two towns are 14cm apart on the map, work out the real distance between them in kilometres.

Constructions & plans

Plans and elevations U3

A **plan** is what is seen if a 3D shape is viewed from above.

An **elevation** is seen if the 3D shape is viewed from the side or front.

Plan A

Front elevation B

Side elevation C

Constructing a triangle U3

To construct this triangle using a compass and a ruler, you would follow these steps:
1. Draw the longest side.
2. With the compass point at A, draw an arc of radius 4cm.
3. With the compass point at B, draw an arc of radius 5cm.
4. Join A and B to the point where the two arcs meet at C.

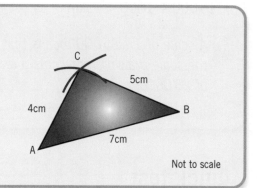

Not to scale

The perpendicular bisector of a line segment U3

To construct the **perpendicular bisector** of the **line segment** XY, you would follow these steps:
1. Draw two arcs with a compass, using X as the centre. The compass must be set at a radius greater than half the distance of XY.
2. Draw two more arcs with Y as the centre. (Keep the compass the same distance apart as before.)
3. Join the two points where the arcs cross.
4. AB is the **perpendicular bisector** of XY.
5. N is the **midpoint** of XY.

The perpendicular from a point to a line U3

To construct the perpendicular from point P to the line AB, you would follow these steps:
1. From P draw arcs to cut the line at A and B.
2. From A and B draw arcs with the same radius to intersect at a point C below the line.
3. Join P to C; this line is perpendicular to AB.

Geometry and measures

The perpendicular from a point on a straight line U3

To construct the perpendicular at the point N on a line:
1. With the compass set to a radius of several cm, and centred on N, draw arcs to cut the line at A and B.
2. Construct the **perpendicular bisector** of the line segment AB as shown on page 86.

Bisecting an angle U3

To bisect an angle, follow these steps:
1. Draw two lines, XY and YZ, to meet at an angle.
2. Using a compass, place the point at Y and draw the two arcs on XY and YZ.
3. Place the compass point at the two arcs on XY and YZ and draw arcs to cross at N.
4. Join Y and N. YN is the **bisector** of angle XYZ.

Constructing an angle of 60° U3

To construct an angle of 60' at point P on a line segment XY, follow these steps.
1. With the compass centred on P, draw an arc which starts just below the line XY and ends almost above point P.
2. Keeping the radius the same, from point M draw an arc to intersect the first arc at point N.
3. Join NP. Angle NPM is 60°.

Construction of an inscribed regular polygon U3

Example
Construct a regular hexagon inside a circle of radius 2cm.

Draw a circle of radius 2cm and mark a point P on its circumference.

Keeping the compass set at 2cm, draw an arc, centre P, which cuts the circle at Q. Q is the centre of the next arc.

Repeat the process until six points are marked on the circumference. Join the points to make a hexagon.

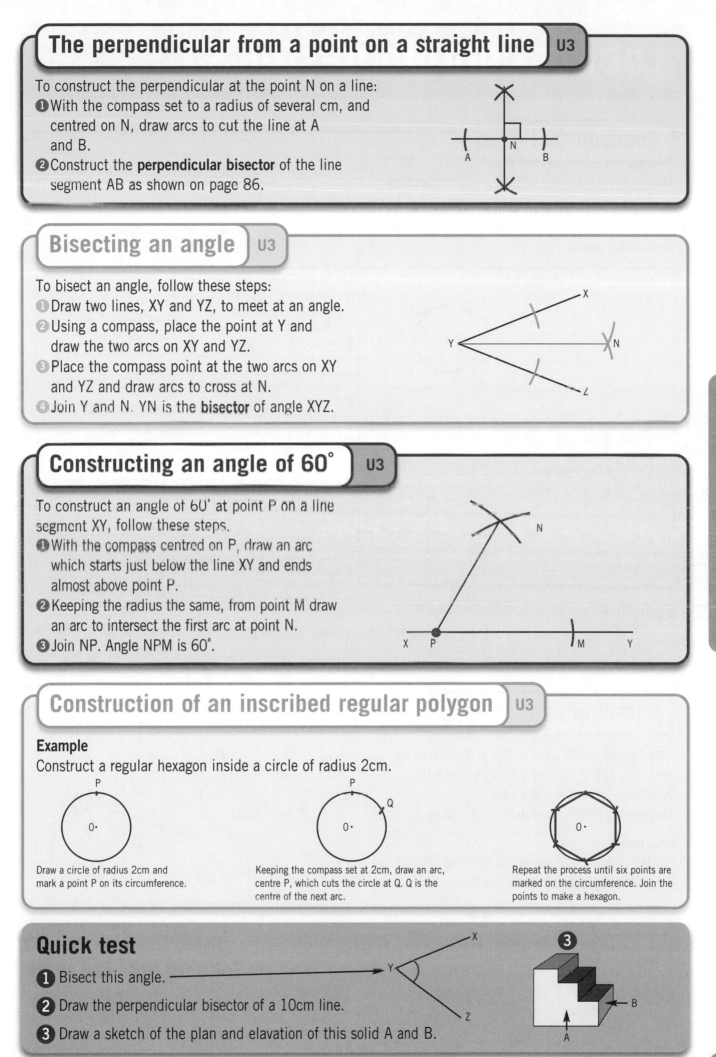

Quick test

1. Bisect this angle.
2. Draw the perpendicular bisector of a 10cm line.
3. Draw a sketch of the plan and elevation of this solid A and B.

Loci & coordinates in 3D

Common loci · U3

The **locus** of a point is the set of all the possible positions which that point can occupy, subject to some given condition or rule. The plural of locus is **loci**.

Remember these points:

The locus of the points that are equidistant from a fixed point P is a circle.

Locus

The locus of the points that are equidistant from two non-parallel lines is the line that bisects the angle formed by the two lines.

Locus

The locus of the points that are a constant distance from a line is a pair of parallel lines above and below the line.

Locus

The locus of the points that are equidistant from two points X and Y is the perpendicular bisector of XY.

Locus

The locus of the points that are equidistant from a line segment XY is a pair of parallel lines above and below XY, and semicircles at either end.

Locus

> *When answering loci questions use the construction techniques previously shown: this will ensure that your work is accurate.*

Coordinates in 3D · U3

Coordinates in 3D involve the extension of the normal x and y axes coordinates into a third direction, known as the z **axis**.
All positions then have three coordinates (x, y, z).

A $(3, 0, 0)$ E $(0, 0, 1)$
B $(3, 2, 0)$ F $(3, 0, 1)$
C $(0, 2, 0)$ G $(3, 2, 1)$
D $(0, 2, 1)$ O $(0, 0, 0)$

Example
For the cuboid, opposite, the vertices would have the following x, y, z coordinates:

Quick test

1. A gold coin is buried in the rectangular field. It is 4m from T and equidistant from RU and RS. Copy the diagram to a scale of 1cm : 1m and mark with an X the position of the gold coin.

Not to scale

Geometry and measures

Angle properties of circles

Circle theorems U3

There are several circle theorems you need to know and be able to apply. The theorems are:

The **perpendicular bisector** of any chord passes through the centre of the circle, O.	The angle at the centre is twice the angle at the circumference, e.g. $P\hat{O}Q = 2 \times P\hat{R}Q$
The angle in a semicircle is always 90°.	Opposite angles of a **cyclic quadrilateral** add up to 180°. (A cyclic quadrilateral is a 4-sided shape with each corner touching the circumference of the circle) i.e. $x + y = 180°$ $a + b = 180°$
The radius and a **tangent** always meet at 90°.	The lengths of two tangents from a point are equal, e.g. RS = RT
Angles in the same **segment** are equal, e.g. $A\hat{B}C = A\hat{D}C$	The angle between a tangent and a **chord** is equal to the angle in the alternate segment (that is, the angle that is made at the edge of the circle by two lines drawn from the chord). This is known as the **Alternate Segment Theorem**. i.e. $a = b$

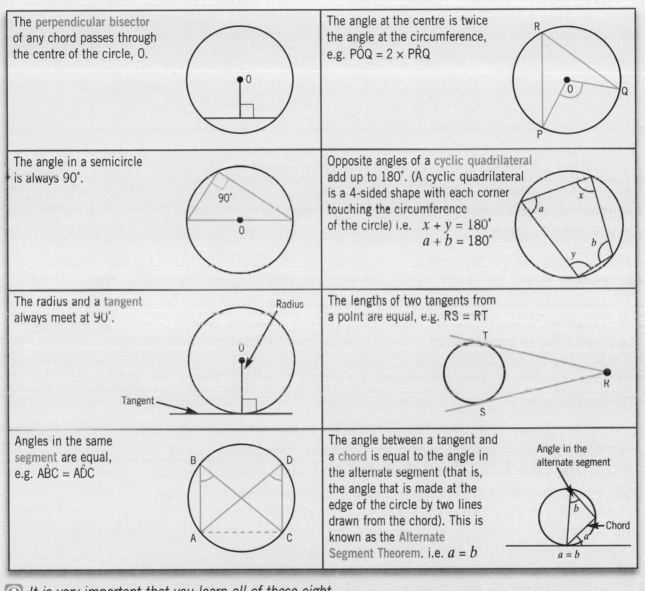

> It is very important that you learn all of these eight theorems and that you can apply and explain them.

Quick test

1. Calculate the missing angles in the diagram.

Pythagoras' theorem

The theorem U3

Pythagoras' theorem states: in any right-angled triangle, the square on the **hypotenuse** is equal to the sum of the squares on the other two sides.

The hypotenuse is the longest side of a right-angled triangle. It is always opposite the right angle.

Using the letters in the diagram, the theorem is written as $c^2 = a^2 + b^2$

This can be rearranged to give $a^2 = c^2 - b^2$ or $b^2 = c^2 - a^2$

These forms are useful when calculating the length of one of the shorter sides.

Finding the length of the hypotenuse U3

Remember: Pythagoras' theorem can only be used for right-angled triangles.

To find the length of the hypotenuse, follow these simple steps:
1. Square the two lengths of the two shorter sides that you are given.
2. Add these two squared numbers.
3. After adding the two squared lengths, take the **square root** ($\sqrt{}$) of the sum to find the hypotenuse.

Example
Find the length of AB, giving your answer to 1 decimal place.

Using Pythagoras' theorem:
$$(AB)^2 = (AC)^2 + (BC)^2$$
$$= 12^2 + 14.5^2$$
$$= 354.25$$
$$AB = \sqrt{354.25}$$
$$= 18.8m$$

Take the square root to find AB.

Round to 1 d.p.

Finding the length of a shorter side U3

To find the length of a shorter side, follow these steps:
1. Square the two lengths of the two sides you are given.
2. To find the shorter length, subtract the smaller value from the larger value.
3. Take the square root ($\sqrt{}$) of your answer.

💡 *Pythagoras' theorem allows us to calculate the length of one of the sides of a right-angled triangle, when the other two sides are known. If you are not told to what degree of accuracy to round your answer, be guided by significant figures given in the question.*

Example
Find the length of FG, giving your answer to 1 decimal place.

Using Pythagoras' theorem:
$$(EF)^2 = (EG)^2 + (FG)^2$$
$$(FG)^2 = (EF)^2 - (EG)^2$$
$$= 27^2 - 18^2$$
$$= 405$$
$$FG = \sqrt{405}$$
$$= 20.1cm \text{ (to 1 d.p.)}$$

If the answer is left as $\sqrt{405}$, it is left in surd form.

Calculating the length of a line AB, given two sets of coordinates — U3

By drawing in a triangle between the two points A (1, 2) and B (7, 6) we can find the length of AB by Pythagoras' theorem.

Horizontal distance = 6   `7 – 1`
Vertical distance = 4   `6 – 2`

$$\text{Length of } (AB)^2 = 6^2 + 4^2$$
$$= 36 + 16$$
$$= 52$$
$$AB = \sqrt{52}$$
$$\text{Length of } AB = 7.21 \text{ (to 2 d.p.)}$$

The midpoint of AB, M, has coordinates (4, 4),
i.e. $\left(\dfrac{1 + 7}{2}, \dfrac{2 + 6}{2}\right)$

The midpoint of a line A (x, y) and B (x_1, y_1) is $\left(\left(\dfrac{x + x_1}{2}\right), \left(\dfrac{y + y_1}{2}\right)\right)$.

Solving problems — U3

Examples

a) Calculate the height of this isosceles triangle.

5cm   5cm
3.5cm

Split the triangle down the middle to make it right-angled.

5cm h
1.75cm

Using Pythagoras' theorem:
$$5^2 = h^2 + 1.75^2$$
$$h^2 = 5^2 - 1.75^2$$
$$h^2 = 21.9375$$
$$h = \sqrt{21.9375} = 4.68\text{cm (to 2 d.p.)}$$

b) A ladder of length 13m rests against a wall. The height that the ladder reaches up the wall is 12m. How far away from the wall is the foot of the ladder?

12m
13m
x

$$13^2 = x^2 + 12^2$$
$$x^2 = 13^2 - 12^2$$
$$x^2 = 169 - 144$$
$$x^2 = 25$$
$$x = \sqrt{25} = 5\text{m}$$

The foot of the ladder is 5m away from the wall.

Quick test

1 Calculate the lengths of the sides marked with x. Give your answers to 1 d.p. 🖩

a)
x
10.2cm
13.8cm

b)
15cm
x
25cm

2 Work out the length of the diagonal of this rectangle. 🖩

15cm
8cm

3 A ship sets off from Port A and travels 50km due north then 80km due east to reach Port B. How far is Port A from Port B by the shortest route? 🖩

Port B
Not to scale
Port A

Trigonometry in right-angled triangles

Trigonometry | U3

Trigonometry in right-angled triangles can be used to calculate an unknown angle or an unknown length.

Labelling the sides of the triangle | U3

A right-angled triangle has three sides:
- **hyp** (**hypotenuse**) is opposite the right angle.
- **opp** (**opposite side**) is opposite the angle θ.
- **adj** (**adjacent side**) is next to the angle θ.
  θ is a Greek letter called **theta** and is often used to represent **angles**.

Trigonometric ratios | U3

The three trigonometric ratios are sine (usually abbreviated to sin), cosine (cos) and tangent (tan):

$$\text{Sin } \theta = \frac{\text{opposite}}{\text{hypotenuse}}$$

$$\text{Cos } \theta = \frac{\text{adjacent}}{\text{hypotenuse}}$$

$$\text{Tan } \theta = \frac{\text{opposite}}{\text{adjacent}}$$

The made-up word **SOH CAH TOA** is a quick way of remembering the ratios. The word comes from the first letters of **S**in equals **O**pposite divided by **H**ypotenuse, etc.

To enter 'sin 30' into the calculator you usually press [sin] [30]. However, some calculators do it backwards, i.e. [30] [sin]. Check your calculator.

Calculating the size of an angle | U3

You may have an [inv] key on your calculator.

Example
Calculate angle ABC.

$$\tan \theta = \frac{\text{opp}}{\text{adj}}$$ Label the sides and decide which ratio you need.

$$\tan \theta = \frac{15}{27}$$ Divide the top value by the bottom value.

$$\tan \theta = 0.\dot{5}$$

$$\theta = 29.1° \text{ (1 d.p.)}$$

On the calculator, key in:

[15] [÷] [27] [=] [shift] [tan] [=]

or, depending on your type of calculator:

[shift] [tan] [15] [÷] [27] [=]

To find the angle, you usually use the second function or shift key on your calculator.

> *Be careful not to round $0.\dot{5}$ to 0.6 as you will get a very different answer.*

> *When calculating the size of an angle, it should usually be rounded to 1 d.p. However, do not round off your answer until right at the end of the question.*

Calculating the length of a side U3

Examples

a) Calculate the length of BC.

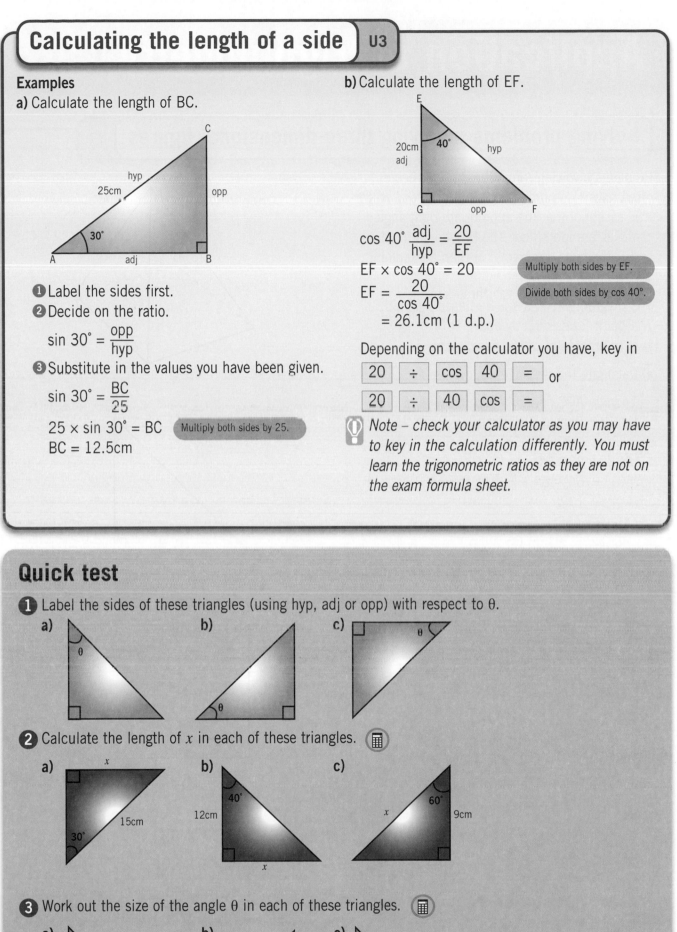

① Label the sides first.
② Decide on the ratio.

$$\sin 30° = \frac{opp}{hyp}$$

③ Substitute in the values you have been given.

$$\sin 30° = \frac{BC}{25}$$

$25 \times \sin 30° = BC$ Multiply both sides by 25.

$BC = 12.5\text{cm}$

b) Calculate the length of EF.

$$\cos 40° \frac{adj}{hyp} = \frac{20}{EF}$$

$EF \times \cos 40° = 20$ Multiply both sides by EF.

$EF = \dfrac{20}{\cos 40°}$ Divide both sides by cos 40°.

$= 26.1\text{cm (1 d.p.)}$

Depending on the calculator you have, key in

| 20 | ÷ | cos | 40 | = | or |

| 20 | ÷ | 40 | cos | = |

⚠ *Note – check your calculator as you may have to key in the calculation differently. You must learn the trigonometric ratios as they are not on the exam formula sheet.*

Quick test

① Label the sides of these triangles (using hyp, adj or opp) with respect to θ.
   a)   b)   c)

② Calculate the length of x in each of these triangles. 🖩
   a)   b)   c)

③ Work out the size of the angle θ in each of these triangles. 🖩
   a)   b)   c)

Geometry and measures

Application of trigonometry

Solving problems involving three-dimensional figures U3

Problems involving three-dimensional figures often have to be broken down into several stages. It is essential that the appropriate right-angled triangles are identified. The trigonometric ratios and Pythagoras' theorem can then be applied.

Example

The diagram shows a square-based pyramid.
The point E lies directly above N.
N is the midpoint of the base.

a) Calculate the distance AC.

Triangle ADC contains a right angle at D.
Using Pythagoras' theorem:
$(AC)^2 = (AD)^2 + (DC)^2$
$(AC)^2 = 8^2 + 8^2$
$(AC)^2 = 64 + 64$
$(AC)^2 = 128$
$\quad AC = \sqrt{128}$
$\quad AC = 11.31\,cm$ (to 2 d.p.)

b) Calculate the height of the vertex E above the base.

Triangle ENC contains a right angle at N.
Using Pythagoras' theorem:
$(EC)^2 = (EN)^2 + (NC)^2$
$(EN)^2 = (EC)^2 - (NC)^2$
$(EN)^2 = 20^2 - 5.65^2...$ (Since NC $= \frac{1}{2}AC = \dfrac{11.31...}{2}$)
$(EN)^2 = 400 - 32$
$\quad EN = \sqrt{368}$
$\quad EN = 19.18\,cm$ (to 2 d.p.)
The vertex E is 19.18cm above the base of the pyramid.

> Make sure you use the unrounded values.

c) Calculate the angle between EC and the base ABCD.

Triangle ENC contains a right angle at N.
$\text{Cos}\,\theta = \dfrac{adj}{hyp} = \dfrac{5.65...}{20}$
$\quad \theta = \cos^{-1}\left(\dfrac{5.65...}{20}\right)$
$\quad\quad = 73.6°$ (to 1 d.p.)

> Check that you know how to use your calculator for trigonometry questions. It is helpful to draw the individual triangle that you are using – this will allow you to label it properly.

Geometry and measures

94

Finding the length of a diagonal in a cuboid | U3

The length of the diagonal of a cuboid of dimensions
$a \times b \times c$ is found by applying Pythagoras' theorem twice.

$$x^2 = c^2 + y^2$$
$$y^2 = a^2 + b^2$$
So $x^2 = c^2 + (a^2 + b^2)$

The length x of the longest diagonal in a cuboid
with dimensions $a \times b \times c$ is:
$$x^2 = a^2 + b^2 + c^2$$

This is a 3D version of Pythagoras' theorem.

Angles of elevation and depression | U3

The **angle of elevation** is
measured from the
horizontal **upwards**.

The **angle of depression**
is measured from the
horizontal **downwards**.

Bearings and trigonometry | U3

Example

In the diagram, A, B and C represent three towns.
The distance AB is 16km. The distance BC is 9km.
Work out the bearing of B from A.

The required bearing is from the North at A.
Find angle BAC.

$$\sin \theta = \frac{\text{opp}}{\text{hyp}} = \frac{9}{16}$$

$$\theta = \sin^{-1} \frac{9}{16}$$

$$= 34.2° \text{ (to 1 d.p.)}$$

Bearing of B from A is $90° - 34.2° = 55.8°$
$$= 0.558° \text{ or } 056°$$

Quick test

1. Dipak stands 30m from the base of a tower.
   He measures the angle of elevation from
   ground level to the top of the tower as 50°.
   Calculate the height of the tower. Give your
   answer to 3 s.f.

2. In the triangle opposite, calculate:
   a) the length of BN.
   b) the length of BC.
   c) the size of angle BCN.

3. The diagram shows a cuboid. Calculate:
   a) the length of HF.
   b) the length of CH.
   c) angle CHF.

Further trigonometry

The sine and cosine rules | U3

The sine rule and cosine rule allow you to solve problems in triangles that do not contain a right angle. By using these rules, you should be able to calculate the length of an unknown side and the size of an unknown angle.

The sine rule

$$\frac{a}{\sin A} = \frac{b}{\sin B} = \frac{c}{\sin C}$$

or

$$\frac{\sin A}{a} = \frac{\sin B}{b} = \frac{\sin C}{c}$$

Labelling the triangle

When labelling the triangle side a is opposite angle A, side b is opposite angle B, etc.

The cosine rule

$$a^2 = b^2 + c^2 - 2bc \cos A$$

or

$$\cos A = \frac{b^2 + c^2 - a^2}{2bc}$$

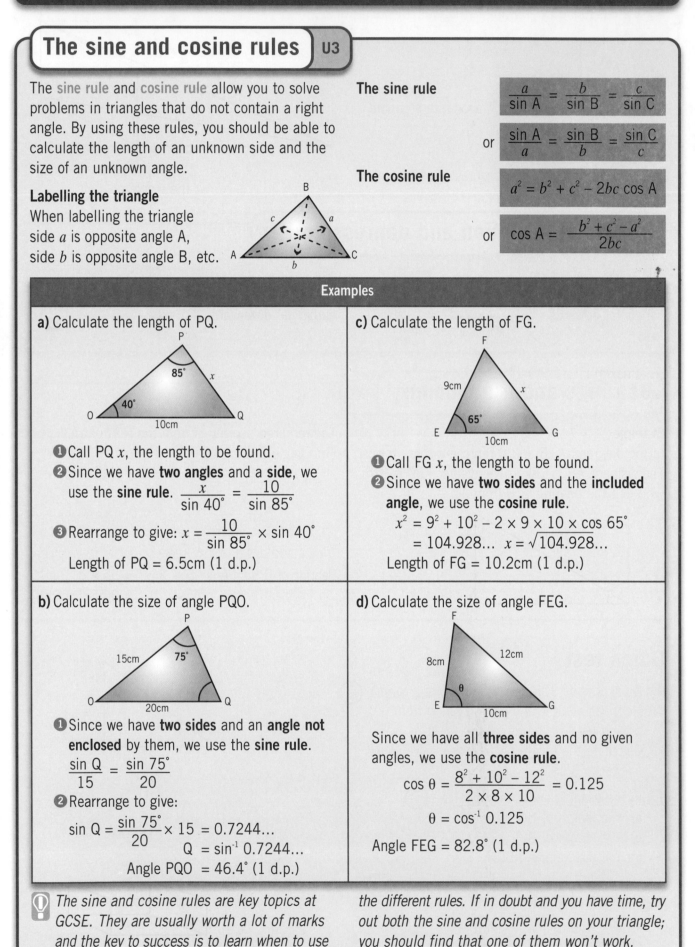

Examples

a) Calculate the length of PQ.

❶ Call PQ x, the length to be found.

❷ Since we have **two angles** and a **side**, we use the **sine rule**. $\dfrac{x}{\sin 40°} = \dfrac{10}{\sin 85°}$

❸ Rearrange to give: $x = \dfrac{10}{\sin 85°} \times \sin 40°$

Length of PQ = 6.5cm (1 d.p.)

b) Calculate the size of angle PQO.

❶ Since we have **two sides** and an **angle not enclosed** by them, we use the **sine rule**.

$$\frac{\sin Q}{15} = \frac{\sin 75°}{20}$$

❷ Rearrange to give:

$$\sin Q = \frac{\sin 75°}{20} \times 15 = 0.7244...$$
$$Q = \sin^{-1} 0.7244...$$

Angle PQO = 46.4° (1 d.p.)

c) Calculate the length of FG.

❶ Call FG x, the length to be found.

❷ Since we have **two sides** and the **included angle**, we use the **cosine rule**.

$$x^2 = 9^2 + 10^2 - 2 \times 9 \times 10 \times \cos 65°$$
$$= 104.928... \quad x = \sqrt{104.928...}$$

Length of FG = 10.2cm (1 d.p.)

d) Calculate the size of angle FEG.

Since we have all **three sides** and no given angles, we use the **cosine rule**.

$$\cos \theta = \frac{8^2 + 10^2 - 12^2}{2 \times 8 \times 10} = 0.125$$
$$\theta = \cos^{-1} 0.125$$

Angle FEG = 82.8° (1 d.p.)

The sine and cosine rules are key topics at GCSE. They are usually worth a lot of marks and the key to success is to learn when to use the different rules. If in doubt and you have time, try out both the sine and cosine rules on your triangle; you should find that one of them won't work.

Geometry and measures

Graphs of trigonometric functions U3

The behaviour of the sine, cosine and tangent functions may be represented graphically as shown below.

y = sin x

The maximum and minimum values of sin x are 1 and -1. The pattern repeats every 360°.

y = cos x

The maximum and minimum values of cos x are 1 and -1. The pattern repeats every 360°. This graph is the same as $y = \sin x$ except it has been moved 90° to the left.

y = tan x

This graph is nothing like the two above. The values of tan x repeat every 180°. The tan of 90° is infinity, i.e. a value so great it cannot be written down.

💡 *Practise drawing the trigonometric graphs. You could be asked to sketch them in the exam.*

The graph transformations (see page 69) can be applied to trigonometric curves.

y = a sin x

Here the points are stretched outwards in the y direction if $a > 1$, as the y coordinates are increased. If $a < 1$, they are pushed inwards, as the y coordinates do not go as high.

y = sin (bx)

Here the points are stretched by a scale factor of $\frac{1}{b}$ parallel to the x axis.

The trigonometric graphs can be used to solve inverse problems.

Example
Solve $\sin x = 0.5$ for values of x between 0° and 360°.

Draw a straight line across the graph at $y = 0.5$ and by its symmetrical properties you can see that the solutions are:

$x = 30°$ and $150°$. (390° is out of the range)

Geometry and measures

Quick test

1 Calculate the missing length or angle marked x in these triangles. 🖩

a)   8cm   x   42°   12cm

b)   11cm   9cm   x   17cm

c)   x   80m   70°   40m

d)   55°   70°   x   60m

2 Find all the solutions of the equation $\sin x = \frac{2}{3}$ in the range $0° < x < 360°$. 🖩

97

Area of 2D shapes

Perimeter and area of 2D shapes U3

The **perimeter** is the distance around the outside edge of a shape.

The **area** is the amount of space a 2D shape covers.

Common units of area are square millimetres (mm^2), square centimetres (cm^2), square metres (m^2), etc.

Areas of quadrilaterals and triangles U3

Area of a rectangle

Area = length × width
$A = l \times w$

Area of a parallelogram

Area = base × perpendicular height
$A = b \times h$
Remember to use the perpendicular height, not the slant height.

Perpendicular height (h)
Base (b)

Area of a triangle

Area = $\frac{1}{2}$ × base × perpendicular height
$A = \frac{1}{2} \times b \times h$

Perpendicular height (h)
Base (b)

Area of a trapezium

Area = $\frac{1}{2}$ × (sum of parallel sides) × perpendicular distance between them
$A = \frac{1}{2} \times (a + b) \times h$ or $A = \frac{1}{2}(a + b)h$

a
Height (h)
b

Examples

a) Find the areas of the following shapes.

i)
5cm   4cm
12cm

$A = b \times h$
$= 12 \times 4$
$= 48cm^2$

ii)
4.9cm   10.1cm
6.2cm

$A = \frac{1}{2} \times (a + b) \times h$
$= \frac{1}{2} \times (4.9 + 10.1) \times 6.2$
$= \frac{1}{2} \times (15) \times 6.2$
$= 46.5cm^2$

b) If the area of this triangle is $56cm^2$, find the height.

Height
16cm

$A = \frac{1}{2} \times b \times h$
$56 = \frac{1}{2} \times 16 \times h$ Substitute the values into the formula.
$56 = 8 \times h$
$h = \frac{56}{8}$ Divide both sides by 8.
So $h = 7cm$

You must learn the formulae in the table (except for the trapezium). You need to know them, otherwise answering the questions will be very difficult.

Changing area units U3

This example will help you to change area units.

The square has a length of 1 metre.
This is the same as a length of 100cm.

Therefore $1m^2 = 10000cm^2$
(not $100cm^2$ as many people think!)

For example. $5m^2 = 5 \times 10000 = 50000cm^2$

1m ↕ 1m — Area = 1m²
100cm ↕ 100cm — Area = 10000cm²

💡 *It's always better to change units before you start a question in order to avoid possible errors.*

Circumference and area of a circle U3

| **Circumference** $= \pi \times$ **diameter** or $C = \pi d$ | **Area** $= \pi \times (radius)^2$ |
| $= \pi \times 2 \times$ **radius** or $C = 2\pi r$ | $A = \pi r^2$ |

Examples

a) The diameter of a circular rose garden is 5m.
Find the circumference and area of the garden.

5m

$C = \pi \times d$
$= 3.14 \times 5$
$= 15.7m$

Substitute in the formula. Use $\pi = 3.14$ or the value of π on your calculator. [EXP] gives the value of π on some calculators.

When finding the area, work out the radius first.
$d = 2 \times r$ so $r = d \div 2$, and $r = 2.5m$
$A = \pi \times r^2$
$= 3.14 \times 2.5^2$

Remember 2.5^2 means 2.5×2.5.

$= 19.625$
$= 19.6m^2$ (3 s.f.)

This answer could be left as 6.25π, i.e. in terms of π.

b) A circle has an area of $40cm^2$. Find the radius of the circle, giving your answer to 3 s.f.
Use $\pi = 3.14$.

$A = \pi \times r^2$
$40 = 3.14 \times r^2$

Substitute the values into the formula.

$\dfrac{40}{3.14} = r^2$

Divide both sides by 3.14.

$r^2 = 12.7388$
$r = \sqrt{12.7388}$

Take the square root to find r.

So $r = 3.57cm$ (3 s.f.)

Check that you can get these solutions with your calculator.

Area diagram: Diameter, Radius, 0

Geometry and measures

Quick test

Work out the areas of the following shapes. Give your answers to 3 s.f.

1 a) 4.2cm, 8.1cm, 12.6cm 🖩

b) 5.3cm, 12cm 🖩

c) 7cm 🖩

d) 15cm, 8cm 🖩

2 Work out the area of the purple shaded region. 🖩
Give your answer to 3 s.f.

10cm

Volume of 3D shapes

Volume U3

Volume is the amount of space a 3D shape occupies.
Common units of volume are mm^3, cm^3, m^3, etc.

Volume of prisms U3

A **prism** is any solid that can be cut across its length into slices, which are all the same shape. The shape of the slices is the **uniform cross-section**.

Volume of a cuboid

Volume = length × width × height
$V = l \times w \times h$

Height (*h*)
Length (*l*)
Width (*w*)

Volume of a prism

Volume = area of cross-section × length
$V = a \times l$

Area of cross-section (*a*)
Length (*l*)

Volume of a cylinder

Cylinders are prisms with circular cross-sections.
Volume = area of cross-section × length (or height)
$V = \pi r^2 \times h$

Radius (*r*)
Height (*h*)

Examples

a) Find the volume of the following 3D shape. Give your answer to 3 s.f.

$V = a \times l$ The area of the cross-section is the area of the triangle
$= (\frac{1}{2} \times b \times h) \times l$
$= (\frac{1}{2} \times 10 \times 7) \times 15$
$= 525 cm^3$

7cm
15cm
10cm

b) The diagram below shows a cylindrical oil drum. Given that 4.5 litres ≈ 1 gallon, what is the volume of oil (in gallons) that is contained in the oil drum? Use $\pi = 3.14$

❶ Work out the volume of the cylinder.
$V = \pi \times r^2 \times h$
$= 3.14 \times 28.75^2 \times 87.5$
$= 227\,098.046\,9 cm^3$

57.5cm
87.5cm

❷ Since $1000 cm^3 = 1$ litre, convert the volume to litres.
$\frac{227\,098.046\,9}{1000} = 227$ litres (3 s.f.)

❸ Now convert to gallons. 4.5 litres ≈ 1 gallon.
$\frac{227}{4.5} = 50.5$

The oil drum contains approximately 50.5 gallons of oil.

Converting volume units U3

Converting volume units is another tricky topic that usually catches students out.

Example

The cube has a length of 1m, which is the same as a length of 100cm. Therefore $1 m^3 = 1\,000\,000 cm^3$ Not quite what you may think! It's probably better, therefore, to change all the lengths to the same unit before starting a question.

1m
1m
1m
Volume = 1m³

100cm
100cm
100cm
Volume = 1 000 000cm³

💡 *For any volume question, work carefully and show each step in your working.*

Surface area of prisms · U3

You need to be able to find the surface area of different prisms.

Cuboid

Length (l), Width (w), Height (h)

To find the surface area of a cuboid, work out the area of each face and then add them together.

$$SA = 2hl + 2hw + 2lw$$

Cylinder

Radius (r), Height (h)

To find the surface area of the cylinder:

$$SA = 2\pi rh + 2\pi r^2$$

Curved surface area — The two circles

Examples

a) Find the surface area of this cuboid.

2cm, 3cm, 5cm

$$SA = 2(hl) + 2(hw) + 2(lw)$$
$$= 2(2 \times 5) + 2(2 \times 3) + 2(5 \times 3)$$
$$= 2 \times (10) + 2 \times (6) + 2 \times (15)$$
$$= 20 + 12 + 30$$
$$= 62\text{cm}^2$$

b) A lampshade is in the shape of a cylinder. The material costs £28 per square metre. How much does the fabric for this lampshade cost?

42cm, 30cm

$$SA = 2\pi rh$$
$$= 2 \times \pi \times 21 \times 30$$
$$SA = 3958.92\text{cm}^2$$
$$SA = 0.395892\text{m}^2$$
$$= 28 \times 0.395892$$
$$= £11.08$$

> In this example, a lampshade will only have the curved surface area.

> Since 1m² = 10000cm²

> Cost of material at £28 per square metre

Quick test

1 Work out the volumes of the following 3D shapes. Give your answers to 3 s.f. 🖩

a)

6.5cm, 27.2cm, 19.8cm

b)

85cm, 10.6cm

2 The volume of a cylinder is 2000cm³ and its radius is 5.6cm. Work out the height to 3 s.f. 🖩

3 Work out the total surface area of the following triangular prism. 🖩

3cm, 5cm, 4cm, 10cm

Further length, area & volume

Advanced topics U3

You need to be able to find the areas and volumes of more complex shapes and solids.

You will be given some of the formulae, but you will need to learn the others.

Arc length, sector area and area of a segment U3

Length of a circular arc
The length of an arc can be expressed as a fraction of the circumference of the circle.

This is the angle of the sector.

Length of arc $l = \dfrac{\theta}{360°} \times 2 \times \pi \times r$

This is the circumference of the circle.

Minor arc means the smaller arc.

For example, length of minor arc:

$l = \dfrac{70°}{360°} \times 2 \times \pi \times 10$

$= 12.2$cm (3 s.f.)

Area of a sector
The area of a sector can be expressed as a fraction of the area of the circle.

Area of a sector $A = \dfrac{\theta}{360°} \times \pi r^2$

This is the area of the circle.

For example, area of minor sector:

$A = \dfrac{70°}{360°} \times \pi \times 10^2$

$= 61.1$cm^2 (3 s.f.)

Area of a triangle
If you know the length of two sides of a triangle and the included angle, you can find the area.

Area $= \frac{1}{2} \times a \times b \times \sin C$

Two lengths   Included angle

For example:

Area $= \frac{1}{2} \times 6.9 \times 10.4 \times \sin 30°$
Area $= 17.9$cm^2 (1 d.p.)

Area of a segment
The area of a **segment** can be worked out in two stages:

❶ Calculate the area of the minor sector and the area of the triangle.

❷ Subtract the area of the triangle from the area of the minor sector.

For example:

Segment area $= (\dfrac{70°}{360°} \times \pi \times 10^2) -$
$(\frac{1}{2} \times 10 \times 10 \times \sin 70°)$

$= 61.1 - 47 = 14.1$cm^2 (3 s.f.)

❗ *If you have the lengths of the radius and chord, you will need to use trigonometry in order to find the angle of the sector.*

Spheres

Volume of a sphere $= \frac{4}{3}\pi r^3$

Surface area of a sphere $= 4\pi r^2$

Example

Find the volume and surface area of a sphere of radius 10cm.

Volume: $V = \frac{4}{3} \times \pi \times r^3$

$= \frac{4}{3} \times \pi \times 10^3$

$= \frac{4000}{3} \times \pi \text{ cm}^3$

$= 4190\text{cm}^3$ (3 s.f.)

Surface area: $SA = 4 \times \pi \times r^2$

$= 4 \times \pi \times 10^2$

$= 400\pi \text{ cm}^2$

$= 1260\text{cm}^2$ (3 s.f.)

Pyramids and cones

A cone is simply a pyramid with a circular base.

Volume of a pyramid $= \frac{1}{3} \times$ area of base $\times$ height

Volume of a cone $= \frac{1}{3} \times \pi \times r^2 \times$ height

Curved surface area of a cone $= \pi r l$ *l is the slant height.*

A frustum is the solid remaining when a cone is cut by a plane parallel to its base and the top cone is removed.

Example

Calculate:

a) the volume of the cone below.

Volume $= \frac{1}{3} \times \pi \times 6^2 \times 8$

$= 96\pi \text{ cm}^3$

$= 301.6\text{cm}^3$

b) the total surface area of the cone.

The slant length needs to be calculated by using Pythagoras' theorem:

$l = \sqrt{8^2 + 6^2}$

$= \sqrt{100}$

$= 10\text{cm}$

Total surface area =
curved surface area + area of circle

$= \pi \times 6 \times 10 + \pi \times 6^2$

$= 60\pi + 36\pi$

Total surface area $= 96\pi = 301.6\text{cm}^2$

You may sometimes be asked to leave your answer in terms of π; that just means leave the π in your calculation instead of working it out.

Always show full working and learn the formulae for arc length and sector area.

Geometry and measures

Quick test

1 Calculate the arc length and sector area of AOB.

2 Calculate the total volume of this solid, leaving your answer in terms of π.

Similarity & congruency

Similar figures U3

Similar figures are those that are the same shape but different sizes. Corresponding angles are equal. Corresponding lengths are in the same ratio. For example:

Notice corresponding lengths are in the same ratio. The lengths of the bigger cone are twice those of the smaller cone.

Corresponding angles are equal.

Finding missing lengths of similar figures U3

Examples

a) Find the missing length a, giving your answer to 2 significant figures.

$$\frac{a}{16} = \frac{9}{12}$$

Corresponding sides are in the same ratio.

$$a = \frac{9}{12} \times 16$$

Multiply both sides by 16.

$$= 12\text{cm}$$

b) Calculate the missing length x.

Drawing the two triangles can be helpful.

$$\frac{x}{6} = \frac{24}{16}$$

Corresponding sides are in the same ratio.

$$x = \frac{24}{16} \times 6$$

Multiply both sides by 6.

$$= 9\text{cm}$$

💡 *Always make sure you put the corresponding sides in the correct order and remember that whatever you are trying to work out must go on the top of the fraction.*

Congruent triangles U3

Two triangles are congruent if one of the following sets of conditions is true (S stands for side, A for angle, R for right angle, H for hypotenuse):

SSS – The three sides of one triangle are the same lengths as the three sides of the other.

SAS – Two sides and the angle between them in one triangle are equal to two sides and the included angle in the other.

RHS – Each triangle contains a right angle. The hypotenuse and another pair of sides are equal.

AAS – Two angles and a side in one triangle are equal to two angles and the corresponding side in the other.

Areas and volumes of similar figures U3

Areas of similar figures are not in the same ratio as their lengths. For example, the corresponding lengths of these squares are in the ratio 1 : 2 but their areas are in the ratio 1 : 4.

A = 1cm²

1

A = 4cm²

2

If the corresponding lengths are in the ratio $a : b$, their areas are in the ratio $a^2 : b^2$.

A similar result can be found when looking at the volumes of similar objects: if the corresponding lengths are in the ratio $a : b$, their volumes are in the ratio $a^3 : b^3$.

For a scale factor n:
- **The sides are n times bigger.**
- **The area is n^2 times bigger.**
- **The volume is n^3 times bigger.**

Examples

a) These two shapes are similar. If the area of the smaller shape is 12cm², calculate the area of the larger shape.

2.3cm

4.6cm

Area = 12cm²

The linear scale factor is 2.3 : 4.6 = 1 : 2
Area scale factor is $1^2 : 2^2$ = 1 : 4
Area of larger shape = 4 × 12 = 48cm².

b) Two cones have surface areas of 9cm² and 25cm². Find the ratio of their volumes.

The area ratio is   9 : 25
so $a^2 : b^2$ = $3^2 : 5^2$
i.e. $a : b$ =   3 : 5

Volume ratio $a^3 : b^3$ = $3^3 : 5^3$
= 27 : 125

💡 *When finding the area and volume of similar figures, always try to work out the linear scale factor. Once you have calculated this, the rest should be easy. If you are given the area or volume scale factor, you will need to take the square or cube root to find the linear scale factor.*

Quick test

1 Find the lengths labelled by the letter x in these pairs of similar shapes. 🖩

a)

9cm

21cm

5cm

x

b)

15.2cm

x

9cm

4cm

2 Two jugs are similar. One holds 100cl and the other holds 200cl. The 200cl jug is 20cm high. Calculate the height of the 100cl jug. 🖩

3 Are these two triangles congruent? Explain why.

9cm

30°

15cm

110°

40°

9cm

15cm

4 The heights of two similar shapes are 4cm and 6cm. If the area of the smaller shape is 40cm², find the area of the larger shape. 🖩

Vectors

Magnitude and direction of vectors — U3

Vectors have both size, or magnitude, and **direction**. Four types of notation are used to represent vectors.

The vector shown here can be referred to as:

$\binom{3}{2}$ or **a** or $\underline{a}$ or $\overrightarrow{AB}$

The direction of the vector is shown on the diagram by using an arrow.

If two vectors are equal then they are parallel and equal in length.

If $\overrightarrow{AB} = k\overrightarrow{CD}$ then $\overrightarrow{AB}$ and $\overrightarrow{CD}$ are parallel and the length of $\overrightarrow{AB}$ is k times the length of $\overrightarrow{CD}$.

If the vector $\mathbf{b} = \binom{4}{3}$ then the vector **-b** is in the opposite direction to **b**. $-\mathbf{b} = -1 \times \mathbf{b} = \binom{-4}{-3}$

The **magnitude** of a vector is the length of the directed line segment representing it. If the vector is expressed in column form, then Pythagoras' theorem can be used to find the magnitude.

In general, the magnitude of a vector $\binom{x}{y}$ is $\sqrt{x^2 + y^2}$

The magnitude of AB is given by:
$$(AB)^2 = 4^2 + 3^2 = 16 + 9 = 25$$
$$AB = \sqrt{25} = 5$$

The magnitude of $\overrightarrow{AB}$ is 5 units.

Other important points — U3

Adding and subtracting vectors
The **resultant** of two vectors is found by **vector addition** or **subtraction**. Vectors must always be combined end to end so that the arrows follow on from each other. A resultant is usually labelled with a double arrow.

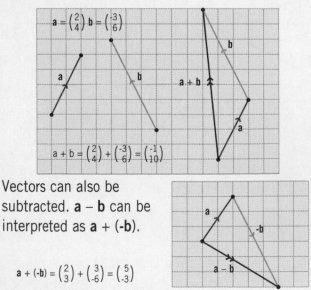

$$a + b = \binom{2}{4} + \binom{-3}{6} = \binom{-1}{10}$$

Vectors can also be subtracted. **a** – **b** can be interpreted as **a** + (**-b**).

$$a + (\text{-b}) = \binom{2}{3} + \binom{3}{-6} = \binom{5}{-3}$$

Splitting vectors into components
Any vector can be split into two components that are at 90° to each other. These two components will be $F \cos \theta$ and $F \sin \theta$.

Position vectors
The position vector of a point P is the vector $\overrightarrow{OP}$ where O is the origin.

In the diagram, the position vectors of C and D are **c** and **d** respectively.

Using this notation:
- $\overrightarrow{CD} = \text{-c} + \mathbf{d}$ or
  $\overrightarrow{CD} = \mathbf{d} - \mathbf{c}$

- $\overrightarrow{OM} = \mathbf{c} + \frac{1}{2}(\mathbf{d} - \mathbf{c})$
  $= \frac{1}{2}\mathbf{c} + \frac{1}{2}\mathbf{d}$
  $= \frac{1}{2}(\mathbf{d} + \mathbf{c})$

where M is the midpoint of CD.

Examples

a)

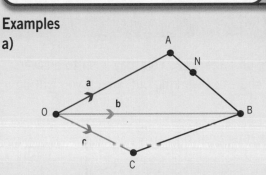

b) OPQ is a triangle.

$$\overrightarrow{OP} = \mathbf{a}$$
$$\overrightarrow{OQ} = \mathbf{b}$$

Given that $\overrightarrow{OA} = \mathbf{a}$, $\overrightarrow{OB} = \mathbf{b}$, $\overrightarrow{OC} = \mathbf{c}$ and that N splits $\overrightarrow{AB}$ in the ratio 1 : 2, find the following vectors:

i) $\overrightarrow{AC}$

$\overrightarrow{AC} = -\mathbf{a} + \mathbf{c}$ (from A to C via O)

ii) $\overrightarrow{AB}$

$\overrightarrow{AB} = -\mathbf{a} + \mathbf{b}$ (from A to B via O)

iii) $\overrightarrow{CB}$

$\overrightarrow{CB} = -\mathbf{c} + \mathbf{b}$ (from C to B via O)

iv) $\overrightarrow{AN}$

$\overrightarrow{AN} = \frac{1}{3}\overrightarrow{AB} = \frac{1}{3}(-\mathbf{a} + \mathbf{b})$

v) $\overrightarrow{ON}$

$\overrightarrow{ON} = \mathbf{a} + \frac{1}{3}(-\mathbf{a} + \mathbf{b}) = \frac{2}{3}\mathbf{a} + \frac{1}{3}\mathbf{b} = \frac{1}{3}(2\mathbf{a} + \mathbf{b})$
(via A)

> *Care needs to be taken when answering vector questions. Always check that the vectors you are using are end to end so that all the arrows follow on from each other and not opposite each other. Always try to simplify your answer as in Example **a)** part **v)** and Example **b)**.*

N is the point on $\overrightarrow{PQ}$ such that PN : NQ = 5 : 2.
Show that $\overrightarrow{ON} = \frac{1}{7}(2\mathbf{a} + 5\mathbf{b})$

❶ Join O to N to form the triangle OPN.
$$\overrightarrow{ON} = \overrightarrow{OP} + \overrightarrow{PN}$$
❷ Now find $\overrightarrow{PN}$.
$$\overrightarrow{PQ} = \overrightarrow{PO} + \overrightarrow{OQ}$$
$$\overrightarrow{PQ} = -\mathbf{a} + \mathbf{b}$$
❸ $\overrightarrow{PN} = \frac{5}{7}\overrightarrow{PQ}$
Hence $\overrightarrow{PN} = \frac{5}{7}(-\mathbf{a} + \mathbf{b})$
Since $\overrightarrow{ON} = \overrightarrow{OP} + \overrightarrow{PN}$ then:
$$\overrightarrow{ON} = \mathbf{a} + \frac{5}{7}(-\mathbf{a} + \mathbf{b})$$
❹ Now simplify:
$$\overrightarrow{ON} = \mathbf{a} - \frac{5}{7}\mathbf{a} + \frac{5}{7}\mathbf{b}$$
$$\overrightarrow{ON} = \frac{2}{7}\mathbf{a} + \frac{5}{7}\mathbf{b}$$
$$\overrightarrow{ON} = \frac{1}{7}(2\mathbf{a} + 5\mathbf{b})$$

Quick test

❶ $\overrightarrow{AB} = \binom{2}{3}$, $\overrightarrow{BC} = \binom{4}{5}$, $\overrightarrow{PQ} = \binom{3}{4}$

a) Show that $\overrightarrow{AC}$ is parallel to $\overrightarrow{PQ}$.

b) Write down the ratio of the length of AC to the length of PQ.

❷ PQR is an equilateral triangle.
M is the midpoint of PR.
$$\overrightarrow{PQ} = \mathbf{p}$$
$$\overrightarrow{QR} = \mathbf{q}$$
Work out in terms of **p** and **q** expressions for the vectors:

a) $\overrightarrow{PR}$　　　b) $\overrightarrow{MQ}$

Practice questions

Use these questions to test your progress. Check your answers on page 112. You may wish to answer these questions on a separate piece of paper so that you can show full working out, which you will be expected to do in the exam.

① Draw the image of the shaded shape after an enlargement by the scale factor $\frac{1}{2}$, with C as the centre of enlargement. Label the image R.

U3

② On a grid:
$\begin{pmatrix} 4 \\ -5 \end{pmatrix}$ translates shape R to shape S
$\begin{pmatrix} 3 \\ -1 \end{pmatrix}$ translates shape S to shape T.

Write down the column vector that translates shape R directly to shape T.

③ A car travels 70 miles in 1 hour 20 minutes. Find the average speed in mph. 🖩

④ A ladder of length 6m rests so that the foot of the ladder is 3m away from a wall. Calculate how far up the wall the top of the ladder reaches. Give your answer to 2 s.f. 🖩

⑤ Calculate the volume of the oil drum, clearly stating your units. Give your answer to 3 s.f. 🖩

125cm
1.58m
Express Oil

⑥ A ladder of length 12m rests against a wall. The angle that the ladder makes with the wall is 40°. Calculate the height of the top of the ladder above the ground, giving your answer to 1 decimal place. 🖩

Ladder   40°

⑦ Elizabeth wants to turf a garden. The shape of the garden is shown. Turf costs £4.50 per square metre. You can only buy a whole number of square metres. How much will the turf cost for Elizabeth to cover the garden? 🖩

4m
6m
5m
8m

⑧ Find the area of the sector AOB. Give your answer to 3 s.f. 🖩

A
5cm
O   55°
5cm
B

⑨ Find the volume of this metal container. 🖩

6cm
20cm   8cm

10 The volume of this cone is 500cm³.
Calculate the length of the radius (*r*). 🖩

30cm

11 The surface area of a cone is 120cm². What is the surface area of a similar cone that is four times as high? 🖩

12 The two spheres are similar. If the volume of the larger sphere is 2145cm³ to 4 s.f., calculate the volume of the smaller sphere. 🖩

3cm   6cm

13 A garden is in the shape of a sector. James wants to put edging along the perimeter of the garden. The edging is sold in pieces 130cm long and 25cm high. James needs enough pieces to fit each side. Each piece costs £7.50. Calculate how much it will cost to put edging around the perimeter of the garden. 🖩

5m   5m
70°

14 Work out the size of the lettered side or angle in each triangle. 🖩

a) 9m
80°
46°
x

b) 12m   13m
x
24m

c) 12.6m   9.4m
72°
x

d) 6cm   80°   5cm
x

15 In the diagram, AB represents a vertical tower on level ground. R and S are two points due west of B. The distance RS is 50m. The angles of elevation of A from S and R are 40° and 60° respectively. Calculate the height in metres of the tower, AB. 🖩

A
40°   60°
S   50m   R   B

16 Calculate length PQ of the diagonal of the cuboid, correct to 1 d.p. 🖩

U   P
T   3cm
N
S
Q   7cm   R   4cm

17 Find the size of each of the lettered angles.

a)
b   O
a   70°

b)
a
b   122°
105°

c)
b
a
62°   85°

d)
a
O   110°
b

Answers

Statistics and probability   Quick test answers

Page 5   Collecting data
1. **Any sensible answer.** Make sure there is a time reference and options/tick boxes.
2. Year 7 – 24, Year 8 – 30, Year 9 – 46

Page 7   Representing data
1. The angles for the pie chart are: Brown 120°, Auburn 60°, Blonde 90°, Black 90°
2. **a)** The frequencies for the heights are: $140 \leqslant h < 145 = 6$, $145 \leqslant h < 150 = 10$, $150 \leqslant h < 155 = 11$, $155 \leqslant h < 160 = 5$, $160 \leqslant h < 165 = 2$
   b) 34 pupils were in the survey
   c) The frequency polygon should be plotted at the midpoints of the bars.

Page 9   Scatter graphs & correlation
1. **a)** Positive correlation   **b)** Zero or no correlation
   c) Negative correlation   **d)** Negative correlation

Page 11   Averages 1
1. Mean = 5; median = 4; mode = 4; range = 7
2. **a)** 1min 19 secs   **b)** 1 min   **c)** 0 mins   **d)** 4 mins

Page 13   Averages 2
1. **a)** 151.56   **b)** $150 \leqslant h < 155$ **c)** $150 \leqslant h < 155$

Page 15   Cumulative frequency graphs
1. **a)** A cumulative frequency graph with the following points should be plotted: (5, 15), (10, 75), (15, 142), (20, 172), (25, 194), (30, 200).
   b) i) approx. 12 miles   **ii)** approx. 9 miles
   c) The median distance travelled is less when Bethany did her survey, but the interquartile range is approximately the same.

Page 17   Histograms
1.

Page 19   Probability 1
1. **Any sensible answer, e.g.:** I will get a 7 when I throw a dice; I will get a 4 when I toss a coin.
2. **a)** $\frac{1}{3}$ **b)** $\frac{4}{9}$ **c)** 0   **3.** $\frac{7}{9}$ **4.** 240   **5.** $\frac{47}{200} = 0.235$

Page 21   Probability 2
1. 0.36
2. **a)**

		1	2	3	4	5	6
	1	1	2	3	4	5	6
Dice 2	2	2	4	6	8	10	12
	3	3	6	9	12	15	18
	4	4	8	12	16	20	24
	5	5	10	15	20	25	30
	6	6	12	18	24	30	36

(Dice 1 across the top)

b) $\frac{4}{36} = \frac{1}{9}$ **c)** 0   **3.** $\frac{24}{49}$

Pages 22–23   Answers to practice questions
1. 0.18
2. **a)**

	Under 13 yrs	13 yrs+	Totals
Boys	15	27	42
Girls	12	21	33
Total	27	48	75

b) 12

3. 60 people   **4.** 3.5
5. **a)** See scatter graph alongside
   b) Strong positive correlation
   c) See scatter graph alongside
   d) About 155.5cm
   e) It is beyond the range of the data

6. **a)**

b) 0.51
c) 0.43

7.

8. **a)** $\frac{12}{42} = \frac{2}{7}$ **b)** $\frac{24}{42} = \frac{4}{7}$

9. **Sensible answers would be:** Lucy will not be able to ask those people who work on a Wednesday morning; people who go to a sports centre generally play sport.

10. **A good answer would include the following points:** the median age of the males is 40 whereas for the females it is 33, hence the males' median age is greater; the interquartile range for the females is much greater than for the males, hence there is a much greater spread of females' ages compared to males' ages; more older females than older males go to the sports centre.

Number   Quick test answers

Page 25   Types of numbers
1. 11, 13, 17, 19, 23, 29   **2.** HCF: 12; LCM: 120   **3. a)** ±8   **b)** 6
4. **a)** $\frac{12}{9}$ **b)** $\frac{p}{x}$

Page 27   Positive & negative numbers
1. 3℃
2. **a)** 4   **b)** -16   **c)** -12   **d)** -12   **e)** 5   **f)** 6   **g)** 7   **h)** -10   **i)** 36

Page 29   Fractions
1. **a)** $\frac{1}{3}$ **b)** $\frac{7}{20}$ **c)** $\frac{6}{13}$ **d)** $1\frac{1}{3}$ **e)** $\frac{5}{21}$ **f)** $\frac{4}{21}$ **g)** $\frac{49}{121}$ **h)** $\frac{50}{63}$
2. £40   **3.** 247mm

Page 31   Decimals
1. **a)** 36.48   **b)** 17.679   **c)** 26.88   **d)** 12.3   **e)** 6   **f)** 52   **g)** 0.4
   h) 0.0037   **i)** 4000   **j)** 45 000   **k)** 470 000   **l)** 32 500
2. **a)** 7.47   **b)** 12.04   **c)** 9.37   **d)** 10.04   **e)** 8.18

Page 33   Approximations & checking calculations
1. **a)** 0.003 79   **b)** 27 500   **c)** 307 000
2. 100   **3.** 10 rolls   **4.** £7.45

Page 35   Percentages 1
1. £210   **2.** 74.6%   **3.** 9.9lb   **4.** £411.76   **5.** Super's; £33.33

Page 37   Percentages 2
1. £170   **2. a)** £1800   **b)** £6180   **3.** £199 500   **4.** £3496.73

Page 38   Fractions, decimals & percentages
1. **i) a)** 0.2857   **b)** 28.57% (2 d.p.)   **ii) a)** 0.6   **b)** 60%
   iii) a) 0.8   **b)** 88.8%
2. 0.041, 5%, 26%, $\frac{1}{3}$, $\frac{2}{5}$, 0.42

Page 39   Recurring decimals & surds
1. **a)** $\frac{15}{99} = \frac{5}{33}$ **b)** $\frac{7}{9}$ **c)** $\frac{281}{990}$
2. **a)** $5\sqrt{3}$ **b)** $10\sqrt{5}$ **c)** $11 - 6\sqrt{2}$ **d)** $4\sqrt{2} - \sqrt{6} + 18$ **e)** $\sqrt{\frac{3}{3}}$

Page 41   Ratio
1. **a)** 4 : 5   **b)** 1 : 2   **c)** 5 : 2   **2.** 10, 15 and 35 sweets respectively
3. £2.76   **4.** 36cm